FIREPOWER

INFANTRY WEAPONS

FIREPOWER

INFANTRY WEAPONS

TACTICAL ILLUSTRATIONS • PERFORMANCE SPECIFICATIONS
FIRST-HAND MISSION REPORTS

EDITOR: CHRIS BISHOP

Grange
BOOKS

This edition first published in 2002 for Grange Books
An imprint of Grange Books plc
The Grange
Kingsnorth Industrial Estate
Hoo, Nr Rochester
Kent ME3 9ND

www.grangebooks.co.uk

ISBN: 1-84013-437-2

Jacket design by
Amber Books Ltd
Bradley's Close
74–77 White Lion Street
London N1 9PF

This material was previously published as part of the
reference set **Firepower**

Printed in Hong Kong

Contents

Introduction

Though it is the large-scale weapons which grab the world's attention, small-arms technology must take an equal ranking in terms of revolutionizing warfare. The machine-guns which scythed down rank after rank of infantry during WWI finally demolished old notions of the individual warrior triumphing by courage and talent alone. In their place came the realization that powerful small-arms could be battle-winning when multiplied across entire units.

The 20th century saw military small arms reach new heights. The bolt-action rifle was much improved, its useable accuracy as a sniper weapon reaching out to one mile in weapons such as the German PSG-1. From the MP28 'trench broom' of WWI, the sub-machine gun evolved into guns such as the compact Uzi or the stunningly accurate MP5 used by the SAS and elite forces worldwide.

Then there is the definitive modern infantry weapon – the assault rifle. Almost every soldier around the world now holds a rifle capable of accurate fire up to 800m. Weapons such as the US M16A2 offer the ability to fire in three-round bursts, as well as grenade-launching attachments. Over 80 million Kalashnikov rifles alone have been produced since the late 1940s, distributed around the world into the hands of armies and terrorists alike. Revolvers and automatic pistols are now made to exemplary standards of manufacture, and provide very reliable firepower to police and soldiers. Finally, machine guns range from the old – but still awesome – Browning .50 calibre weapon to light machine guns such as the Minimi, which can be carried easily into combat by one man.

Firepower: Infantry Weapons takes a close look at what separates the small-arms expert from the common soldier who knows little more than how to point and shoot. It explores the individual small-arms which have left their impact on modern warfare, as well as looking through first-hand accounts at the terrible effects small-arms can have on the battlefield. **Firepower: Infantry Weapons** is a complete account of the tactics and technology of personal weaponry.

A BGM-71 TOW anti-tank missile is captured on camera milliseconds after its launch. The TOW is a Tube-Launched Optically-Tracked Wire-Guided system in which the operator visually flies the missile onto its target.

This SEAL trooper is wearing cutting edge hostage rescue/urban combat gear, including a ballistic-nylon helmet with internal communications, fast-rope harness (with glove attached to stop rope-burn) and the redoubtable Heckler & Koch MP5 sub-machine gun.

SPECIAL FORCES
Sub-Machine Guns

Some say that the modern assault rifle puts paid to the sub-machine gun. But there is one type of unit that still needs a weapon that combines compact size with controllable, maximum firepower – the Special Forces.

S pecial Operations soldiers carry them on deep penetration missions behind enemy lines, and the SAS has used them in making dramatic hostage rescues in full view of the world's television cameras. You see them in the hands of the police at international airports, but you don't see them in the entourage of the President of the United States. His bodyguards keep them hidden, under the dashboards of their cars, or in innocent-looking briefcases.

They come in a variety of shapes and sizes, but sub-machine guns all have one thing in common. They provide the maximum amount of controllable short-range firepower in the smallest possible package.

Evolution of the sub-machine gun

Sub-machine guns evolved during World War I. In the confined, close quarter fighting

The black, pressed-steel Uzi is typical of modern sub-machine guns, even though the design is well over 30 years old.

of the trenches, troops needed a special kind of weapon: a compact gun, capable of automatic fire like a machine-gun, but that would be less of a handful in a trench than a bayonetted rifle. There were a number of designs, but the German Bergmann MP18 was the first really practical weapon to reach the troops.

Even today, more than 70 years after the end of that war, the MP18 displays the classic characteristics of the sub-machine gun. It fired a pistol cartridge from a simple 'blowback' mechanism. The low-power ammunition meant that it was relatively easy to control when firing on full auto; an important characteristic since a light weapon would be

9

hard to control with full-power ammo.

Since then, sub-machine guns have appeared with a variety of complexity and finish. They have ranged from the beautifully manufactured Steyr-Solothurn, made in Switzerland in the 1930s, to utilitarian designs turned out by the million during World War II. The most primitive guns, such as the British Sten gun, looked to be thrown together out of gas-pipe and pressed steel.

No role in the modern world?

However, the development of the assault rifle at the end of the war seemed to signal the end of the line. The trouble with sub-machine guns is that they are inaccurate. They are fine for spraying bullets as long as you don't mind where they go. The famous Tommy-Gun was even nicknamed the 'trench broom' by its designer because that was how he saw it being used. But people don't fight in trenches any more.

It could be argued that there is no military role for the weapon these days. Carbine versions of the latest assault rifles are hardly larger than sub-machine guns, and can seemingly do everything that the simpler gun does, only more accurately and over longer distances. Yet not only is the sub-machine gun still in existence, but more and more designs are being marketed every year.

Part of the reason is that sub-machine guns are easy to make and maintain. It's much cheaper to build large numbers of simple weapons than to tool up for the more complex and expensive manufacture of sophisticated assault rifles.

A new type of war

But there is now a new type of war, and a new type of warrior. The alarming rise in national and international crime and terrorism has brought the battlefield to the streets of the cities of the world.

Security forces who are fighting this battle cannot, except in exceptional circumstances, use conventional weapons. What they require is a weapon which is small enough not to be obvious on the streets and easy to handle in confined spaces, such as in vehicles or buildings. It must have enough stopping power to handle an armed criminal or terrorist, yet not be so powerful as to harm innocent bystanders half a mile away.

Clandestine warriors

Special Forces also particularly need such weapons. When you are on foot behind enemy lines, loaded with communications gear and explosives for some clandestine demolition work, you need simple, tough, reliable, firepower that doesn't weigh too much. And even further into the shadowy world of clandestine warfare, there is a need for guns that can fire silently. The easiest way to do that is to fit a silencer onto a gun that fires subsonic pistol-type ammunition, with a longer range than a silenced pistol, but one that is not so clumsy in confined spaces as a full-sized rifle.

The sub-machine gun lives

The sub-machine gun is the only practical weapon that comes near to matching all these needs, even though some examples are actually designed for very different reasons. The classic Uzi was produced in the 1950s when the fledgling state of Israel needed all the firepower it could get as quickly as pos-

Above: The small, boxy Ingram sub-machine guns are now an old design, and their light weight and high rate of fire make them difficult to control on full auto. Firing short bursts from the shoulder with stock extended makes the Ingrams accurate enough for security purposes, however, and a number of Special Forces and police hostage rescue teams use the weapon.

Right: The Beretta PM 12 is a popular sub-machine gun that has achieved considerable export success. Post-war construction methods make the Beretta over 4 lb lighter than the Thompson gun (see box below), but no less effective. Grooves inside channel any dirt and debris, keeping the gun working even in bad conditions.

THE THOMPSON:
First of the many

Designed for the US Army in World War I, the Thompson was the first successful SMG. But it appeared too late for military service, and first saw action in the hands of US police. To the dismay of its designer, General John Thompson, the weapon soon became notorious as the classic gangster gun in 1920s Chicago and the favourite weapon of the IRA.

The Thompson came into its own during World War II when the US Army needed all the weapons it could get. It was also supplied to British and Allied forces, and saw action on all fronts. But the Thompson was still a relatively expensive weapon to make, and all armies soon adopted very cheaply made SMGs such as the British Sten gun.

FLASHBACK

A Marine 'Tommy gunner' covers his buddy on Okinawa in 1945. Although heavy, the Thompson was valued for its reliability.

SPECIAL FORCES Sub Machine Gun Reference File

1

AUSTRIA

Steyr MPi

At first glance, the **Steyr MPi 69** looks like an Uzi clone, and in many ways it is. The Austrian sub-machine gun has the same style of boxy body as the Uzi, with the magazine feeding through the pistol grip. However, it is not exactly the same, being a simpler weapon designed to be sturdy and easy to manufacture.

The MPi 69 has a number of unusual features. First trigger pressure fires single shot; pull the trigger back all the way for automatic fire. The applied safety is a cross bolt which passes through the receiver. Pressed to the right by the thumb, it projects out to one side and shows a white 'S' for safe. Pressed to the left a red 'F' shows, releasing the trigger. In the

By using the pistol grip to house the magazine, the Steyr MPi has a longer barrel than the Beretta although the total length remains the same. This is the MPi 81, distinguished by the cocking handle on the left of the receiver.

middle, the safety allows semi-auto fire only. The sling is attached to the cocking lever and the gun is cocked by pulling back on the sling. To lessen the chance of accidents, however, a later model known as the **MPi 81** has a conventional cocking handle. It also has an increased rate of fire.

Specification
MPi 69
Calibre: 9-mm Parabellum
Weight: 7.8 lb (loaded, with 32-round magazine)
Length: 26.4 in (18.3 in with butt retracted)
Barrel length: 10.24 in

Muzzle velocity: c. 1,250 ft per second
Rate of fire (cyclic): 550 rounds per minute
Magazine: 25- or 32-round box
Users: Austrian army

SUB-MACHINE GUNS:
The Professionals' View

"The modern professional soldier isn't likely to carry a sub-machine gun as his weapon of choice, but that's due mostly to the improvements in modern assault rifle design. When he does, it will be to take advantage of the strengths of the SMG – the round that it uses, the extra capacity of its magazine, and sometimes the improved accuracy he'll get from a barrel a bit longer than a pistol's.

"There are times when you just don't want to use the small-calibre, high-velocity rounds of assault rifles. In a room full of terrorists the object is to stop each and every subject immediately, before he can pull a trigger or press the button on a remote-control detonator. For that you need large-calibre rounds that travel at relatively low speeds and either mushroom or break up on impact.

"Hit the subject with an assault rifle round and it's quite likely to go straight through him, sometimes without him even knowing it, leaving him able to fight on. On top of that, the damage caused by 5.56-mm rounds penetrating brick walls and flying around the streets is definitely to be avoided!"

Special Warfare Instructor

sible. The quickest way to do that was to build sub-machine guns. But the Uzi's small size, easy maintenance and tough reliability have made it a favourite with Special Forces teams around the world. By contrast, the Heckler & Koch MP5 is a scaled-down version of a successful German assault rifle, and is much more complex than other sub-machine guns. But it is very accurate, and in the skilled hands of the SAS has proved deadly.

2

Beretta Model 12

ITALY

Beretta sub-machine guns have always been superbly made, and were among the most sought after trophies of World War II. The **Beretta Model 12**, introduced in the late 1950s, was different. For the first time, the company used stamped metal parts and a tubular receiver. Although it looked simple, it was made to the usual high standard.

Making use of a wraparound bolt, the Model 12 is a compact but accurate weapon. Although it sold well, by the 1970s it had been replaced by the **Model 12S**. This looks much the same as the earlier gun, but has an improved selector lever and a new epoxy resin finish, making it much more durable.

The Model 12 was issued to Italian

Like many SMGs the Beretta PM 12 has a grip safety – this is the prominent catch on the pistol grip just below the trigger guard. It reduces the chance of an accidental discharge, since you must be holding the weapon for it to fire.

special forces, and is a popular choice with hostage rescue units around the world. It has been exported widely, to countries including Gabon, Libya, Nigeria, Saudi Arabia, Tunisia and Venezuela. The Model 12 is also licence built in Belgium, Brazil, and Indonesia.

Specification
Beretta Model 12
Calibre: 9-mm Parabellum
Weight: 8.4 lb (loaded, with 32-round magazine)
Length: 26 in (16.45 in with stock folded)

Barrel length: 7.87 in
Muzzle velocity: 1,250 ft per second
Rate of fire (cyclic): 500-550 rounds per minute
Magazine: 20-, 32-, or 40-round box
Users: Italian Special Forces and Carabinieri

ACCURACY, RANGE AND EFFECT

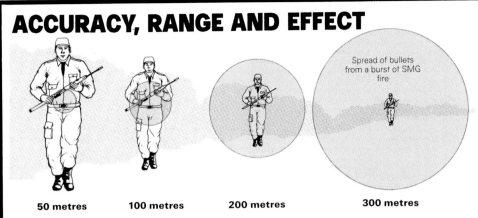

Spread of bullets from a burst of SMG fire

50 metres **100 metres** **200 metres** **300 metres**

Sub-machine guns, with their short barrels and low-power rounds, are not long-range weapons. At 50 metres a good shot will be able to keep all the bullets in a burst in a circle 25-cm across. Even at 100 metres, when the burst spreads out over 50 cm, most of the bullets will hit a man-sized target. The probability of hitting that same target decreases dramatically as the range increases to 200 or 300 metres.

Below: A US Secret Service agent, Uzi in hand, calls for assistance just after President Reagan is shot in Washington in 1981. His finger extended outside the Uzi's trigger guard indicates that the weapon is cocked and ready for firing.

Right: Off-camera flash and a long exposure reveals the muzzle climb you get when firing on full auto. Each shot forces the weapon up and to the right, making bursts of more than three or four rounds very hard to keep on target.

The only problem with the MP5 is the very complexity which makes it accurate. As long as you give it a thorough cleaning after every action, it will perform reliably and effectively. But give it the kind of battering that a soldier will subject it to in the field, and it will cease to function. For a battlefield weapon, this is a serious problem. Hostage rescues are different. Action rarely last for more than a few minutes, and the troops who take part are all highly skilled weapons handlers. Accuracy is more important than the ability to fire after a week of mishandling which weapons have to survive in the field.

Sub-machine guns have been manufactured in a number of countries over the years. The

---

3   ITALY

Spectre

Urban terrorism has been a significant factor in Italian life for many years. SITES, a new company based in Turin, has developed a sub-machine gun specifically for counter-terrorism and unconventional war.

The **Spectre** has been designed with a number of innovations which make it unlike anything else on the market today. It has a patented four column magazine, containing 50 rounds but taking up as little space as a more conventional 30-round box. It fires from a closed bolt, making it more accurate than most other sub-machine guns. It has a double action facility; when cocked, the hammer remains at the rear of the receiver, but a de-cocking lever allows it to move forward under

Right: The Spectre is one of several new sub-machine guns to appear during the 1980s in response to the increased demand from police and paramilitary units.

control without firing. While it is safe to carry in this state, pressure on the trigger will retract the hammer and allow the weapon to fire.

To overcome the chamber heating associated with closed bolt weapons, the Spectre has a forced draught system, the movement of the bolt drawing cool air in from the rear when firing and so keeping barrel temperatures down.

Specification
Spectre
Calibre: 9-mm Parabellum
Weight: 6.4 lb (unloaded)
Length: 22.8 in (13.8 in with stock folded)
Barrel length: 5.12 in
Muzzle velocity: c. 1,310 ft per second
Rate of fire (cyclic): 850 rounds per minute
Magazine: 30- or 50-round four-file box
Users: sales mainly throughout Europe

---

4   FINLAND

Jati-Matic

One of the most interesting machine pistols to have been produced in recent years is the striking **Jati-Matic** from Finland.

One of the main problems with small automatic weapons is that they are hard to control on full auto. The Jati-Matic tackles the problem by having the bolt recoil upwards at an angle from the barrel, forcing the weapon down and negating the effect of muzzle-climb. The shape also means the pistol grip is set higher than normal, aligning the firer's hand with the barrel. This makes the Jati-Matic one of the few SMGs with which one-handed automatic fire is possible.

A folding foregrip under the barrel is also the cocking handle. Like the Steyr,

The unusual shape of the Finnish Jati-Matic is an attempt to overcome the SMG's biggest weakness: the tendency of the muzzle to climb off-target during automatic fire.

the first pressure on the trigger fires single shots, and pulling the trigger fully back against a spring stop fires automatic.

The Jati-Matic is offered with a full range of accessories, including a silencer and a laser aiming device.

Specification
Jati-Matic
Calibre: 9-mm Parabellum
Weight: 4.3 lb (loaded, with 20-round magazine)
Length: 14.76 in
Barrel length: 8 in
Muzzle velocity: 1,180-1,312 ft per second
Rate of fire (cyclic): 600-650 rounds per minute
Magazine: 20- or 40-round box
Users: Finnish army

Argentine FMK-3 has a similar mechanism to the Uzi, while the Australian F1 is unique for having a top-loading magazine. The Steyr MPi69 looks like the Uzi, but is simpler. Steyr also produce a sub-machine gun version of their AUG rifle. Brazil's arms industry produces a number of workable designs, while China's Type 63 is a silenced weapon for clandestine use. The Czech Model 23 is no longer made, but was the inspiration for the Uzi. Finland's Jati is notable for its small size, while the French MAT 49 is a rugged design that is found all over the French-speaking world. Walther and Heckler & Koch produce sub-machine guns in West Germany, with H&K designs also being produced under licence in Greece. Israel's Uzi is famous, as are the designs Beretta produces in Italy. Other Italian SMGs include the Franchi, Spectre, and AGM-1. The tiny PM-63 produced in Poland found favour with clandestine forces in Eastern Europe, but it is no longer being made. South Africa has produced a number of designs, as has Star in Spain. The British Sterling is an old design in service in more than 90 countries. The Ingrams 9 is probably America's most famous post-war design, but American industry makes

---

5

USA

Ingram Model 10

You've all seen the movie. One of the bad guys, cornered by the forces of law and order, whips out a small, boxy sub-machine gun and starts hosing out lead. The chances are that the weapon he is using will have been designed by Gordon Ingram, and it would be easy to regard it as nothing but a Hollywood toy. But the Ingram sub-machine gun is definitely not a toy.

Ingram's **Model 10** first appeared in the late 1960s, and its small size and high rate of fire led to its use by special forces in Vietnam. Since then it has been adopted by security forces around the world.

Largely made from steel stampings, the Ingram is a simple weapon to produce. It copies features found in the

Right: The famous Ingram is now popular with Colombian drug traffickers and the gangs of Los Angeles as well as with military units.

Israeli Uzi and the Czech cz 23, most notably the telescoping bolt which reduces the weapon's overall length, and the magazine housing inside the pistol grip. The Ingram has had a chequered production history, with a number of companies building the guns at one time or another. More recently, SWD Inc has offered the 9-mm **M-11** and the diminutive **M-11A1** in .380 (9-mm short). Both with 16- or 30-round magazines.

Specification
Ingram Model-10
Calibre: 0.45-in ACP
Weight: 8.4 lb (loaded, with 30-round magazine)
Length: 11.6 in (21.57 in with stock extended)
Barrel length: 5.75 in

Muzzle velocity: 850 ft per second
Rate of fire (cyclic): c. 1,000 round per minute
Magazine: 30-round box
Users: Special Forces including the British SAS

6

GERMANY

Walther MP

Walther has long been a name to conjure with in the field of small-arms design, but in 1945 the company went into temporary eclipse, most of its factories being in East Germany. By the early 1960s, however, the company was back in business, and in 1963 introduced a new 9-mm sub-machine gun, the **Walther MP**.

A compact, well made weapon, the MP was made in two versions, the **MP-L** with a 10.12-in barrel and the **MP-K**, with a 6.73-in barrel. It is a simple blowback sub-machine gun, largely manufactured from steel stampings in the modern fashion.

The first users of the MP were the West German navy and the Federal German police. Latin America has

In addition to its well-known range of pistols, the Walther company's post-war range included the MP series sub-machine guns, which have been widely sold in South America.

proved to be the best export market, with the Mexican navy acquiring Walther MPs, followed by the military forces of Brazil, Colombia and Venezuela.

Specification
MP-L
Calibre: 9-mm Parabellum
Weight: 8 lb (loaded, with 32-round magazine)
Length: 29 in (17.9 in with stock folded)
Barrel length: 10.12 in

Muzzle velocity: 1,300 ft per second
Rate of fire (cyclic): 550 rounds per minute
Magazine: 32-round box
Users: Columbia, Brazil and Venezuela

Several Arab countries are so impressed with the Israeli Uzi that they pay huge sums of money to acquire them secretly on the international market

all kinds of SMGs, from the simplest weapons to the highest of high-tech designs.

For years to come

Small, cheap and easily concealed, the modern sub-machine gun is one of the most important tools for combatting the urban terrors of the 21st century. Technology may have changed its appearance in the last few years, and the people using it are a far cry from the German Stormtroopers of 1918, but the sub-machine gun of today is still the same handy package of firepower first seen over 70 years ago.

Right: German security personnel fire their Heckler & Koch MP5s from a Mercedes during training in the 1970s. At this time, the main threat was from the Baader-Meinhof terrorists, who were also armed with MP5s stolen from government armouries.

Below: The SMG has found increasing employment amongst police units, where its short-range fire power makes it useful in urban sieges. Here, Uzi and shotgun armed Tennessee police have brought a hostage situation to a violent end.

Combat Comparison

Uzi

Like the Ingram, the **Uzi** has been adopted by Hollywood, which tends to hide the fact that it is one of the most successful sub-machine guns ever built.

Born out of the turmoil of Israel's early days, the Uzi was designed by Lieutenant Uziel Gail. He copied the wraparound bolt and the pistol grip magazine housing from the innovatory Czech vz 23, and produced a sturdy weapon that was easy to manufacture and could be relied on even in the most arduous conditions.

Uzis are used extensively by the highly efficient Israeli Defence Forces. The German Army is equipped with a version manufactured under licence by Fabrique Nationale in Belgium. Uzis have been widely exported. Many security organizations have chosen the weapon. Most notably the Presidential protection agents of the US Secret Service.

The **Mini-Uzi** and **Micro-Uzi** are smaller versions of the standard weapon, designed to be suitable for concealment by police and security personnel. They retain all the characteristics which make the Uzi one of the best sub-machine guns available today.

Specification
Uzi
Calibre: 9-mm Parabellum
Weight: 9 lb (loaded, with 32-round magazine)
Length: 25 in (17 in with stock folded)
Barrel length: 10.25 in
Muzzle velocity: 1,250 ft per second
Rate of fire (cyclic): 600 rounds per minute
Magazine: 25-, 32-, or 40-round detachable box
Users: military and police forces worldwide including Israel and Germany

Heckler und Koch MP5

On 5 May 1980 the siege of the Iranian embassy in London was ended by the sinister black-clad figures of the SAS. Sharing the glare of publicity with the normally reclusive British troopers was their choice of weapon; the **Heckler und Koch MP5**.

Unlike most other sub-machine guns, the MP5 fires from a closed and locked bolt, using the same delayed blowback action as the successful G3 rifle. Although this makes it more expensive to produce and maintain than simpler guns, any disadvantage is offset by greatly increased safety and accuracy. This is why the MP5 is overwhelmingly the weapon of choice for the world's elite Hostage Rescue Teams, and is widely used by other special operations units.

Current models of the MP5 include the **MP5A2** with fixed plastic stock, the **MP5A3** with a sliding metal strut stock, the **MP5SD2** and **MP5SD3**, which are silenced versions of the same weapons, the very short **MP5K**, and the **MP5KA1**, which is a special version with no protrusions that is designed to be carried under clothing.

Specification
MP5A2
Calibre: 9-mm Parabellum
Weight: 6.55 lb (loaded, with 30-round magazine)
Length: 26.77 in
Barrel length: 8.86 in
Muzzle velocity: c. 1,100 ft per second
Rate of fire (cyclic): 800 rounds per minute
Magazine: 15- or 30-round box
Users: German Special Forces; numerous police and Special Forces worldwide

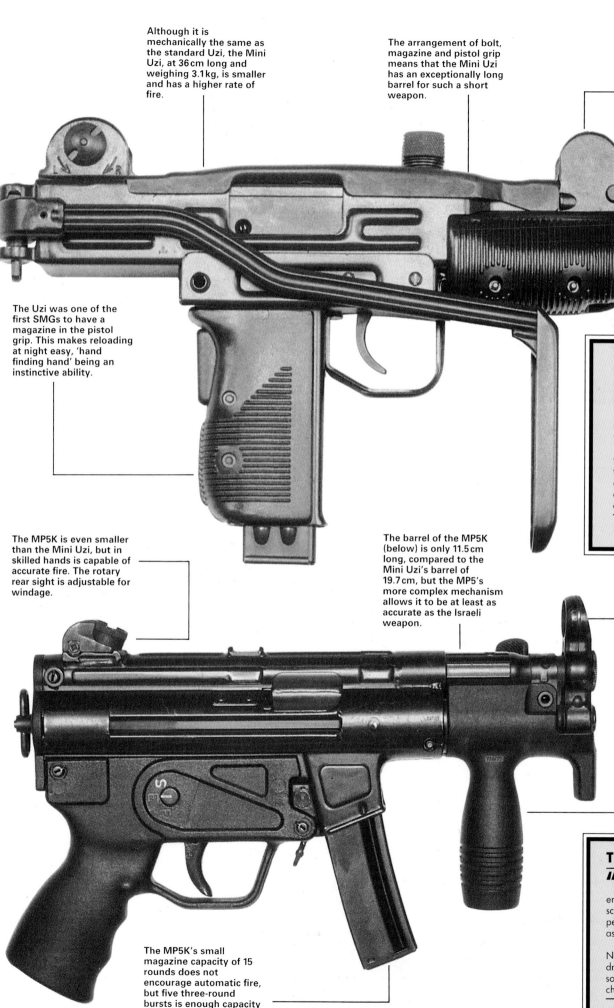

Although it is mechanically the same as the standard Uzi, the Mini Uzi, at 36cm long and weighing 3.1kg, is smaller and has a higher rate of fire.

The arrangement of bolt, magazine and pistol grip means that the Mini Uzi has an exceptionally long barrel for such a short weapon.

The Mini Uzi has the same sights as the standard Uzi, with a cut-out in the cocking handle to allow a clear view between front and rear.

The Uzi was one of the first SMGs to have a magazine in the pistol grip. This makes reloading at night easy, 'hand finding hand' being an instinctive ability.

The MP5K is even smaller than the Mini Uzi, but in skilled hands is capable of accurate fire. The rotary rear sight is adjustable for windage.

The barrel of the MP5K (below) is only 11.5cm long, compared to the Mini Uzi's barrel of 19.7cm, but the MP5's more complex mechanism allows it to be at least as accurate as the Israeli weapon.

The ring foresight is a standard Heckler & Koch feature, but some MP5Ks have had them removed so as to allow snag-free carrying in clothing or a holster.

The short barrel leaves little room for a foregrip, so forehand grip is added. This gives the firer maximum control in all kinds of fire.

The MP5K's small magazine capacity of 15 rounds does not encourage automatic fire, but five three-round bursts is enough capacity for a single engagement.

The professionals' view

"Getting a bit long in the tooth, now. When it first appeared, the Uzi's cyclical rate of fire had everybody amazed. It was so much faster than anything that had been around before. But now we take that sort of performance for granted.

"Its relative simplicity keeps it attractive for semi-pros, though. It's much more forgiving than the Heckler — but that doesn't mean you can drop it in the sand and expect it to come up firing every time, as has sometimes been suggested!"

Special Warfare Instructor

The professionals' view

"The MP5 is so typical a modern German product! It's precision-engineered down to the knurling on the last screw. The fit of every part to every other is perfect. You feel it every time you strip and assemble the weapon.

"But that, in itself, can cause problems. Neglect it, leave it uncleaned after use, drop it, leave it knocking around somewhere, and there's a very good chance that it will fail on you."

Special Warfare Instructor

WEAPONS AND EQUIPMENT OF THE
SAS
COUNTER REVOLUTIONARY WARFARE KIT

Special Air Service teams choose their weapons very carefully – especially when engaged in the role of counter-revolutionary warfare.

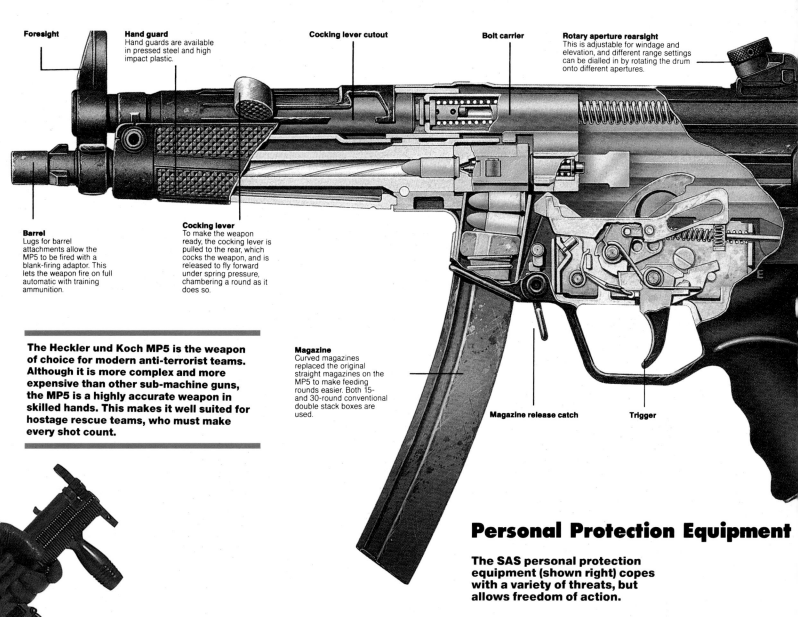

Foresight

Hand guard
Hand guards are available in pressed steel and high impact plastic.

Cocking lever cutout

Bolt carrier

Rotary aperture rearsight
This is adjustable for windage and elevation, and different range settings can be dialled in by rotating the drum onto different apertures.

Barrel
Lugs for barrel attachments allow the MP5 to be fired with a blank-firing adaptor. This lets the weapon fire on full automatic with training ammunition.

Cocking lever
To make the weapon ready, the cocking lever is pulled to the rear, which cocks the weapon, and is released to fly forward under spring pressure, chambering a round as it does so.

Magazine
Curved magazines replaced the original straight magazines on the MP5 to make feeding rounds easier. Both 15- and 30-round conventional double stack boxes are used.

Magazine release catch

Trigger

The Heckler und Koch MP5 is the weapon of choice for modern anti-terrorist teams. Although it is more complex and more expensive than other sub-machine guns, the MP5 is a highly accurate weapon in skilled hands. This makes it well suited for hostage rescue teams, who must make every shot count.

Left: This sinister figure could be the last thing a terrorist sees. The equipment developed by the SAS for CRW and hostage rescue has been widely copied by other law enforcement agencies. The trooper carries stun grenades, a pistol, a sub-machine gun and a knife. The clothing is fire-resistant and he is wearing body armour. In addition to this basic kit the team would also be equipped with CS gas grenades, shotguns, sniper rifles and grenade launchers.

Personal Protection Equipment

The SAS personal protection equipment (shown right) copes with a variety of threats, but allows freedom of action.

The elite soldiers of the SAS are prepared for anything, from raiding behind the lines to secret intervention all over the world. But since their dramatic victory at the Iranian Embassy in London in 1980, they are best known for their anti-terrorist role. They call it Counter Revolutionary Warfare (CRW), and deploy a carefully selected range of weapons for such desperate close-quarter fighting.

The battle must be won in minutes, if not seconds, or the terrorists will have time to murder their hostages. Weapons have to be deadly accurate but also short and handy: racing through cluttered rooms with a full-size rifle is a recipe for disaster. Ammunition must be powerful enough to kill the enemy but not so powerful that it could pass clean through or ricochet, endangering innocent lives.

The primary weapon of the SAS CRW teams is the German Heckler & Koch MP5 sub-machine gun. It's an unusual SMG because its working parts stop moving just before the weapon fires. In most sub-machine guns, a bolt travels forward inside, strips a round from the magazine and fires it all in one go. This movement alters the balance of the gun and makes it difficult to aim steadily. By using the same system of operation employed in their rifles, H&K have produced a much more accurate weapon.

Soft-nosed devastation

The ultra-modern MP5 fires 9-mm Parabellum, a popular military cartridge introduced in 1903. In a short-range shootout it is devastating, particularly when using soft-nosed bullets. Although less effective than the American .45 bullet, because it is smaller, up to 30 rounds can be fitted in a magazine. SAS troopers carry three magazines and use the same type of ammunition in their pistols.

Even the world's most reliable SMG may jam or there may be no time to spare for a reload. So the SAS also carry the 13-shot Browning HP35 pistol. It may be over 50 years old, but it remains the standard sidearm of the British Army. Each trooper carries two magazines on his thigh and one in an elasticised wrist strap known as the 'wristrocket'.

Victim blinded

For all the skill of the soldiers, the holed-up terrorist can still have the odds stacked in his favour. Barricaded in a room, he can cover the door or window and shoot down anyone breaking in. The solution is the 'stun' grenade or 'flash-bang'. The noise is so loud it can perforate eardrums and the flash leaves a victim temporarily blinded. Detonation in a confined space like a room or airliner maximises the effect. It gives the SAS trooper, ears protected and eyes shaded by his gas mask, a few seconds' advantage. And that is all he needs.

Far left, main pic: Monday, 5 May 1980. The SAS counter-revolutionary warfare team smashes its way into the Iranian Embassy at Princes Gate in London. With stun grenades and bursts of fire from their German machine pistols, they bring the Embassy siege to a dramatic conclusion.

Parabellum performance

The Uzi fires the 9-mm Parabellum round, the most common sub-machine-gun round in use. Its virtue in the Uzi is a controllable recoil that enables the user to fire this small gun at full-auto yet still retain control over aiming. The 9-mm performance is poor when compared to assault rifles – effective range is usually under 100m (328ft) – but the weight of fire under these distances makes the impact a powerful one.

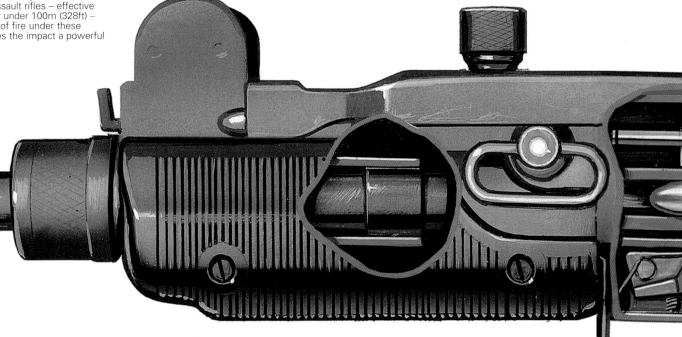

Mini- and Micro-Uzi

An even smaller version of the Uzi, appropriately called the Micro-Uzi, was developed in the 1980s. This gun is only 600mm (23.62in) long with the stock extended; fold the stock and the gun is a mere 360mm (14.17in). Even smaller than this is the Micro-Uzi at 460mm (18.1in) stock extended, 250mm (9.84in) stock folded. Because of its very light bolt which has little resistance to the pressure of the blowback, the Micro-Uzi fires at 1250rpm, emptying its magazine in less than second.

Operation

The Uzi is a blowback-operated weapon, a common form of operation in submachine guns. The 9-mm Parabellum round is held in the chamber purely through the inertia of the bolt. Upon firing, the recoil force imparted on the cartridge pushes the bolt back until its movement is arrested and reversed by the recoil spring. As it travels back the bolt strips the next round from the top of the magazine and chambers it.

Uzi SMG

The infamous Uzi sub-machine gun has a justifiable claim to have revolutionized the world of gun design. Despite being only 470mm (18.5in) long in its stock-folded position, it can spray out 9-mm rounds at a cyclic rate of 600rpm. This combination of compact dimensions and heavy firepower has made the Uzi a massive worldwide export success to special forces and counter-terrorist police units, as well as falling into the hands of terrorists and criminals.

Construction

The Uzi was designed at a time when Israel was looking for a cheap method of arming its forces (during the late 1940s it was armed with a wide-ranging mix of war surplus weaponry). Consequently the Uzi makes use of economical steel pressings and stampings, with components often being pinned together. These processes were far cheaper than machining, in which the gun parts are cut from solid blocks of metal – a very wasteful process which requires skilled machinists.

HECKLER & KOCH MP5

Sling swivel
A double loop adjustable slip is usually fitted, which allows the weapon to hang securely across the chest ready for instant use while both hands are free for abseiling, climbing etc.

Stock variations
This fixed stock is usually used for police duty and special operations in Northern Ireland. For CRW the SAS uses either the telescoping stock version, the MP5A1, or the MP5K with no stock at all.

Sear
In automatic fire the sear holds the hammer down just long enough for the breech to close. The cyclic rate of fire is about 800 rounds per minute, or 13 rounds per second.

Helmet
The National Plastics AC 100/1 ballistic composite helmet provides an advanced head protection system for special forces. It is made up from layers of ballistic cloth and will protect the head from blows, falling masonry and a variety of small-arms fire.

Stun grenades
usually blow out all the lights, so this torch is vital for target acquisition in a darkened room full of smoke. The torch has a grip switch pad on the pistol grip so it can be switched on to take the shot and then instantly released, so it is difficult for the terrorist to pinpoint the position of the trooper in the room.

Avon Industrial Polymers SF 10 respirator
The SF 10 was designed specifically for special forces use in internal security operations. It offers high levels of protection against incapacitating agents with low breathing resistance. There are two canister mounts, allowing two canisters to be used or one canister in combination with an air escape bottle. The tough eyepieces have detachable anti-flash outsert lenses.

Heckler & Koch MP5 SMG
This weapon is ideal for close-quarter battle. It is light, short, easy to handle and accurate. While 9-mm Parabellum is not particularly deadly, the probability of multiple hits on a terrorist make up for the individual bullets' lack of ballistic efficiency.

The Armourshield GPV/25 armoured vest
Will protect the wearer from grenade fragments and small-arms fire. It comprises a ceramic contoured plate front and back and a layered Kevlar fragmentation vest providing all-round cover, including high under the arms, so the trooper is not exposed when returning fire. A blunt trauma shield is built into the armour.

9-mm Browning magazines
The instant back-up weapon of all team members is usually the 9-mm Browning High Power pistol, although individuals are free to choose their model of Browning or another pistol altogether if they wish.

Fire-retardant suit
This GD Specialist Supplies fire-retardant body protection system will provide a high degree of protection from flash blast and heat injury caused by fire or by explosion or incendiary devices.

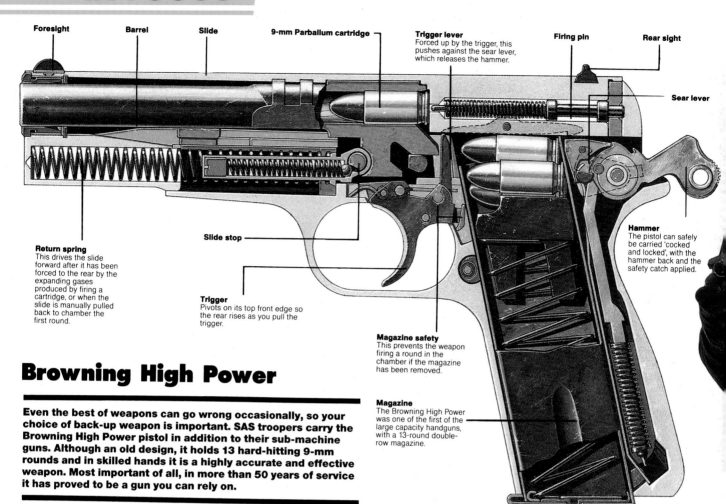

Foresight

Barrel

Slide

9-mm Parballum cartridge

Trigger lever
Forced up by the trigger, this pushes against the sear lever, which releases the hammer.

Firing pin

Rear sight

Sear lever

Return spring
This drives the slide forward after it has been forced to the rear by the expanding gases produced by firing a cartridge, or when the slide is manually pulled back to chamber the first round.

Slide stop

Trigger
Pivots on its top front edge so the rear rises as you pull the trigger.

Hammer
The pistol can safely be carried 'cocked and locked', with the hammer back and the safety catch applied.

Magazine safety
This prevents the weapon firing a round in the chamber if the magazine has been removed.

Magazine
The Browning High Power was one of the first of the large capacity handguns, with a 13-round double-row magazine.

Browning High Power

Even the best of weapons can go wrong occasionally, so your choice of back-up weapon is important. SAS troopers carry the Browning High Power pistol in addition to their sub-machine guns. Although an old design, it holds 13 hard-hitting 9-mm rounds and in skilled hands it is a highly accurate and effective weapon. Most important of all, in more than 50 years of service it has proved to be a gun you can rely on.

One SAS squadron is permanently assigned to Counter Revolutionary Warfare (CRW) and hostage rescue. Each of the regiment's squadrons serves in turn, ensuring that every trooper has experience in the field and can be called on if more men are required. The CRW squadron, known as the Special Purpose team, has four operational troops, each with one officer and 15 men, divided into four-man teams that are further divided into two pairs.

The tactics used are based on conventional military house-clearing techniques. Superb marksmanship and team co-ordination is necessary to instantly identify and eliminate threats hidden amongst hostages, often in darkness or in smoke-filled rooms.

"Room clear!"

Typically, one pair will enter a room, covered by the second pair. Tossing in stun grenades, the first pair will make their entry rapidly along a pre-planned route. Once they report the room is secure the second pair move through to the next room. At no time should any member of the team be exposed to fire without his partner being able to instantly return accurate fire.

The SAS was the first to develop stun grenades, which rely on flash, smoke and sound to neutralise ter-

A four-man entry team goes in. Note the variety of weapons – Heckler & Koch MP5k, Mini Uzi, Browning pistols with 20-round magazines fitted, and one .45 Colt government auto pistol!

rorists without seriously injuring hostages.

Each team has a specific task in an operation, from the surveillance specialists who find out everything they can about a target before an assault, through the containment and sniper teams that provide security during an assault, to the assault teams themselves. Although each man has been trained to fulfil a particular specialized role, in practice most SAS troopers can perform any of the tasks if necessary.

Abseiling
Rather than dropping a rope down the side of a building before he assaults, the trooper keeps the rope in a bag suspended by his foot to avoid giving the enemy advance warning by flashing a black rope past the window.

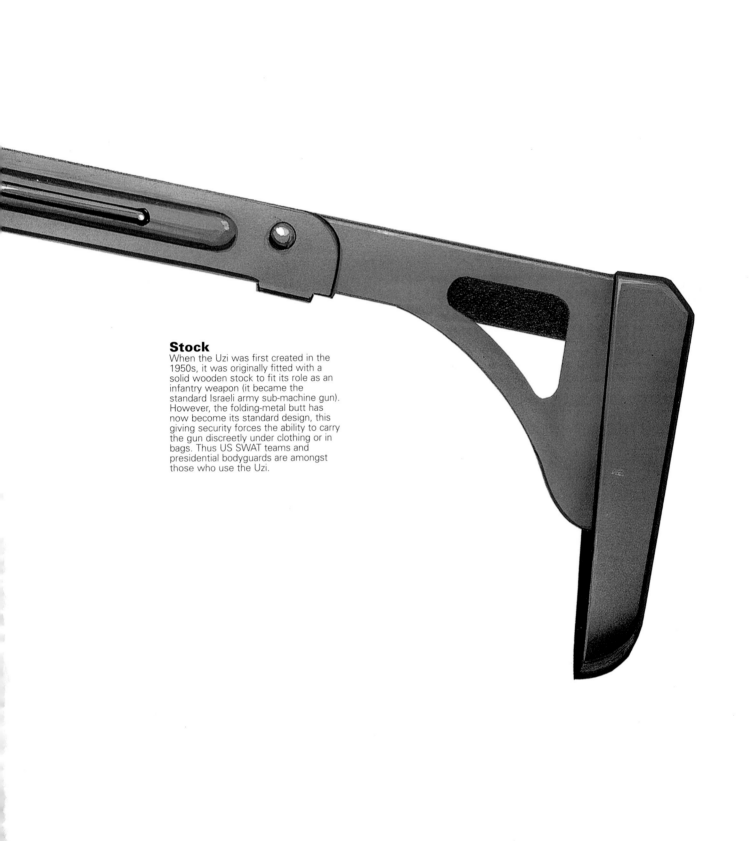

Stock

When the Uzi was first created in the 1950s, it was originally fitted with a solid wooden stock to fit its role as an infantry weapon (it became the standard Israeli army sub-machine gun). However, the folding-metal butt has now become its standard design, this giving security forces the ability to carry the gun discreetly under clothing or in bags. Thus US SWAT teams and presidential bodyguards are amongst those who use the Uzi.

Wrap-around bolt

The Uzi's small dimensions are achieved by virtue of a wrap-around bolt. On conventional weapons the bolt face sits flush against the end of the barrel, but on the Uzi the front part of the bolt actually overlaps the end of the barrel. This dramatically compresses the overall length of the gun. Uziel Gal, the designer of the Uzi, also sited the magazine housing in the pistol grip to further shorten the weapon.

Feed

The Uzi is fed via a conventional 9-mm box magazine, though this is inserted into the pistol grip rather than having a separate housing. The intention behind this arrangement is to reduce length but also make the gun more easily loaded in dark conditions – the magazine is simply aimed towards the base of the hand. An upshot of this arrangement is that the pistol is incredibly well-balanced and can be easily handled without the folding stock extended for support.

Operating the Uzi

First hold the Uzi in your right hand at about a 60° angle to the right, exposing the magazine housing aperture in the pistol grip. Insert a fresh magazine and push it up with a final slap to lock it into place. Then squeeze in the grip safety on the back of the grip, and with your left hand pull back the cocking lever on the top of the gun and release. All that remains is to set the safety switch to a fire position. Aim and pull the trigger.

COUNTER REVOLUTIONARY WARFARE KIT

The basic CRW (Counter Revolutionary Warfare) entry team consists of four men, like an infantry fire team. Each man has his own specific tasks within the team and is armed and equipped to do a highly specialised job.

Body armour
Heavy armour against high-velocity rifle rounds is only worn by the last two men in the team, as they are most likely to take rounds - terrorist speed of reaction is reckoned not to be fast enough to catch the first two men in. All the team are protected from low-velocity weapons such as pistols, SMGs and shotguns.

Pump-action shotg[un]
These (manufactured [by] Winchester and Remington) are popula[r] choices for use at clos[e] quarters in a house. In [an] emergency, the shotgu[n] can be used to blow o[ff] hinges and locks on do[ors] in order to gain entry. [It] can also fire a variety [of] ammo: buckshot - six [to] eight lead balls per sh[ot,] deadly at close range, [a] solid rifled slug, or eve[n] CS gas.

Load-carrying assault vest
This is usually manufactured to the individual's specification. Kit carried varies from stun grenades, aircrew knives for cutting through abseil rope in an emergency, ammunition, and entry kit such as cut-down sledgehammers and bolt cutters.

Climbing harness
A lightweight climbing harness is worn beneath the body armour. This is a combination of a sit harness supporting the pelvis and a chest harness, which prevents the wearer ending up upside down if things go wrong. The harness features a strap at the back of the neck which can be used to drag or winch the soldier out of trouble should he become a casualty.

BODY ARMOUR

Armourshield GPV/25 armoured vest

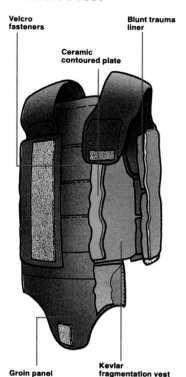

- Velcro fasteners
- Blunt trauma liner
- Ceramic contoured plate
- Groin panel
- Kevlar fragmentation vest

National Plastics AC 100/1 ballistic composite helmet

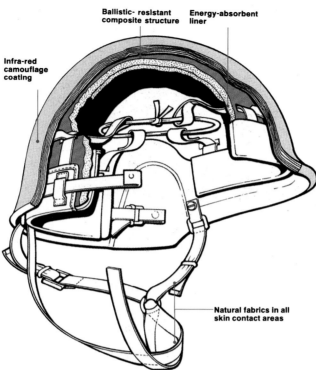

- Infra-red camouflage coating
- Ballistic-resistant composite structure
- Energy-absorbent liner
- Natural fabrics in all skin contact areas

Below: The hard armour vest is designed to stop high-velocity armour-piercing rifle rounds, as long as they hit the ceramic plate. The rest of the vest will stop low-velocity bullets and fragments. The blunt trauma shield absorbs the energy from the bullet: the model (inset) shows the effect if a .357 Magnum pistol bullet shot through a vest into Plasticine both with and without a trauma shield. Impressive stuff.

Above: The protective headgear will stop low-velocity projectiles, as will the shield, which will happily absorb multiple hits while the shield man fires back through the slot. When moving, the shield man should always be covered by his oppo.

Left: The shield has taken fire from close range. The arm is protected by a blunt trauma shield.

Below: The Browning High Power is still the favourite for the job. The one in the foreground is a target version with a longer barrel and target sights.

SAS
Hostage Rescue

5 May 1980. The black-clad figures smashed their way into the Iranian Embassy in London. In full view of the TV cameras, Britain's elite SAS troopers were about to justify their reputation as the best hostage rescue team in the world.

Above: SAS *troopers cover the outside of the Embassy as the assault teams go in. If the terrorists try to flee to safety, security teams like this ensure that they won't get far.*

Right: *A police marksman, covering the* **SAS** *assault on the front of the building, watches the escape of* **BBC** *sound man Sim Harris as explosions and gunfire erupt from within the Embassy.*

SAS troopers on the roof of the Embassy prepare to go down the rear of the building on ropes, from where they will smash their way in on two levels.

In May 1980, inside the Iranian embassy, SMGs burst onto the world stage in the hands of the professionals – Britain's SAS.

The terrorist leader put down the telephone. As far as he was concerned the siege of the Iranian Embassy in London was over. The British government had agreed to his terms: he and his group were to be escorted to Heathrow and on to an airliner to fly to freedom. Then came the sound of breaking glass. One terrorist went to find out what was going on. He went out of sight round a corner, and there was a sudden burst of gunfire. A magazine of 9-mm rounds from the H&K MP5 sub-machine gun in the hands of a black-clad SAS trooper had almost cut him in half. His siege was over.

Patience snapped

For six days in the spring of 1980 the staff of the Iranian Embassy had been held hostage by six Arab terrorists. The gunmen were demanding autonomy for the Arab-speaking Province of Khurzistan in Iran, where, they claimed, their countrymen were being unfairly treated by the government of Ayatollah Khomeini. The hostages taken in London included four Britons, one man employed by the Embassy, two BBC men who had been applying for visas to visit Iran, and PC Trevor Lock, a member of the police Diplomatic Protection Group. Five hostages had been released during the course of the siege, but 20 remained in captivity on Sunday 4 May. The next day, Bank Holiday Monday, found 16 men and four women still held hostage. Then the terrorists' patience snapped.

A hostage dies

Fed up with the delaying tactics of the British government, the terrorists murdered the Embassy Press Officer at 1.30pm. The body was dumped outside the front door and the chilling announcement made that one hostage would be shot every 45 minutes until the British gave in. Letting the terrorists succeed was out of the question: the only option was to storm the building and free the hostages.

Although surveillance devices, poked through the walls from adjacent buildings, had pinpointed where most of the hostages were being held, no-one could be certain where each terrorist and each innocent civilian was. Some of the terrorists were holding guns on the hostages. Somehow, they had to be dealt with so quickly that they would not have the time to shoot their prisoners.

The motto of the SAS is 'Who dares wins', and the attack they had prepared demanded a very special kind of daring.

Two teams

The main assault was launched from the roof where, on the very first day of the siege, SAS men had examined the squat chimneys and decided that it was possible to abseil – sail down on ropes – down the back of the building and smash into the Embassy through the ground- and first-floor windows. Simultaneously, another team would move from the front balcony of a neighbouring house on to the front balcony of the Embassy and break into the Chargé d'Affaires' office on the first floor. The two groups would then converge on the second-floor rooms where the majority of the hostages were believed to be held. However, the windows through which the SAS planned to

EYE WITNESS

"I put my back against the door. The windows had been covered throughout the siege but I could see a chink of daylight. I peeped through the shutters. To my right was a man dressed like a frogman. Black mask, black uniform and boots. He said, 'Get down, get down!' I lay down flat. He kicked the windows in and threw two crackers in. He was followed by two more. I shouted, 'Get in there, lads, and get them'."

Harris crawled out onto the balcony to escape the smoke and gas. He heard a voice from below.

"'That's Harris, that's Harris. Stay flat, stay flat.' It came from a man with a gun, behind a wall."

Beckoned across to another balcony, Harris was taken into an office, from where:

"I was thrown out of the building from one man to another in a chain. They got hold of us and threw us out of the back. We were tied up with locking straps, and told not to say a word. I thought the soldiers might not be able to identify the hostages. I saw them trying to decide about one gunman. I shouted, 'There is no doubt, he is a terrorist!' He was taken away.

"At first, I did not know what was going on. I did not know that it was the SAS. I knew that they must be a crack commando squad. I would like to tell the soldiers, 'Thank you for my life. God knows what would have happened in the embassy if you had not come in as you did.'"

Sim Harris, BBC sound engineer:hostage.

The Assault

enter the building had been armour-plated to protect the Embassy staff from attack! Within hours of the siege beginning, SAS men had been poring over plans of the building, studying the layout until they knew it by heart. Looking at photographs, they memorised the faces of the known hostages: once inside the building, they would have to make split-second decisions that would spell life or death for the occupants.

A hitch in time

Military operations seldom go exactly according to plan, and the storming of the Iranian Embassy was no exception. The first hitch came when one of the abseiling team attacking the back of the building accidentally put his boot through a third-floor window on the way down. The noise alerted the terrorist leader on the telephone, and sent one of his group to investigate. He drew a Walther P.38 automatic pistol but did not notice the powerful figure of PC Lock follow him. As the whole building suddenly resounded to the noise of stun grenades, the terrorist went into the Ambassador's office and saw the two SAS men climbing in through the armoured window, which had been smashed by pre-prepared explosives. He aimed his pistol but was brought down by a flying rugby tackle from PC Lock. A violent struggle ensued as the policeman tried to draw the revolver he had managed to keep hidden throughout the siege. Then the SAS men were inside, and one shouted 'Trevor! Leave off!'. Lock rolled away. The trooper fired his MP5, and the terrorist was shot dead.

Another dead terrorist

The troopers Lock had helped out were the second of three pairs abseiling down the back of the building. The first pair landed in the back garden and blew in the windows. Racing for the staircase they encountered one terrorist lurking by the front door, shot him down and charged upstairs. Hurtling across the landing they cornered the terrorist leader in a secretary's office and emptied two full magazines into him.

But one of the troopers was in trouble. Before the assault it was realised that they had not brought enough climbing rope, and the balance had to be made up with different rope bought in London. But under the strain it ravelled into a knot, leaving him swinging short of his target. The CS gas canisters flung into the Embassy

created a dense cloud of choking smoke to add to the terrorists' problems, but they also set fire to the heavy curtains. The unfortunate trooper was dangling suspended in the flames until the men on the roof cut his rope. He dropped into the garden, picked himself up and dashed inside.

Upstairs on the second floor the terrorists realised what was happening. Their bluff had been called. Two of them promptly

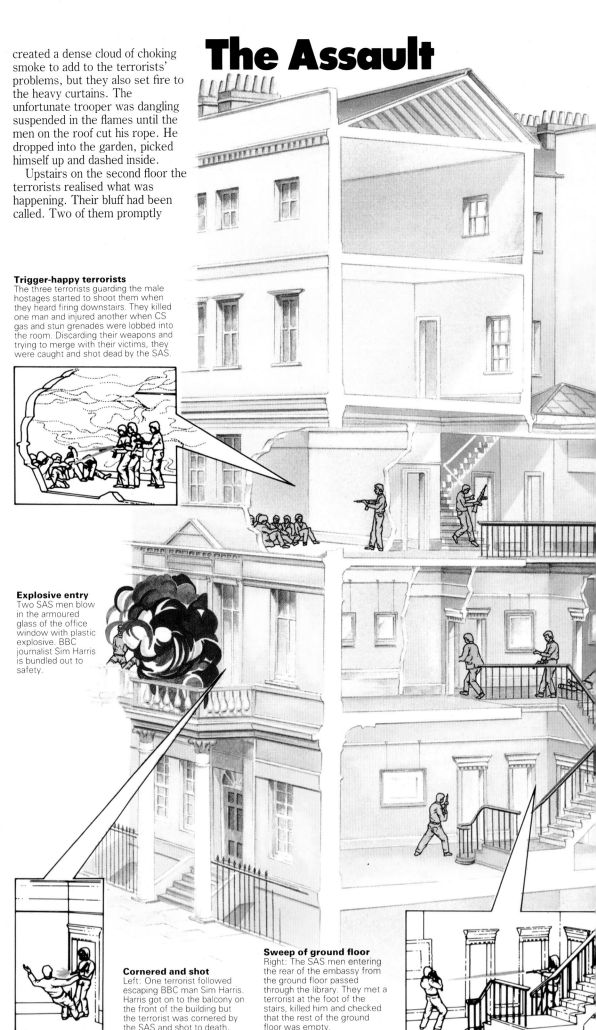

Trigger-happy terrorists
The three terrorists guarding the male hostages started to shoot them when they heard firing downstairs. They killed one man and injured another when CS gas and stun grenades were lobbed into the room. Discarding their weapons and trying to merge with their victims, they were caught and shot dead by the SAS.

Explosive entry
Two SAS men blow in the armoured glass of the office window with plastic explosive. BBC journalist Sim Harris is bundled out to safety.

Cornered and shot
Left: One terrorist followed escaping BBC man Sim Harris. Harris got on to the balcony on the front of the building but the terrorist was cornered by the SAS and shot to death.

Sweep of ground floor
Right: The SAS men entering the rear of the embassy from the ground floor passed through the library. They met a terrorist at the foot of the stairs, killed him and checked that the rest of the ground floor was empty.

This cutaway shows how the SAS attacked the Iranian Embassy. One team attacked from the front, breaking in through the first-floor windows. Other two-man teams abseiled down the back of the building and entered on the ground and first floors. The inset drawings show each stage of the 10-minute gun battle that followed.

Surviving terrorist
The female hostages were being guarded by one terrorist on the landing. When the SAS attacked he rushed inside the room and hid. He was eventually bundled downstairs with the prisoners and only identified when all survivors were lying in the garden. He was the only terrorist to survive.

Abseiled descent
One of the two pairs of SAS men that abseiled down the back of the building dropped on to the rear balcony and broke through the window.

Blown entry
The other pair descended to ground level and blew their way into the library before clearing the embassy's ground floor.

Roll and shoot
PC Trevor Lock rugby-tackled one of the terrorists sent by their leader to investigate the noises at the rear of the building. He was grappling with the terrorist when an SAS man arrived on the first floor. He ordered Lock to roll clear and killed the terrorist.

machine-gunned the male hostages sitting on the floor in the telex room: the Assistant Press Attaché was killed, the Chargé d'Affaires was hit in the face and legs but survived. The doorman had a very lucky escape when a 50-pence piece in his trouser pocket stopped a bullet from inflicting a very nasty wound indeed. He was then knocked to the floor by a smoke grenade that flew in through the window and struck him in the chest. A concussion grenade followed, stunning many of the hostages as well as breaking the morale of the terrorists. In an abrupt change of heart they threw some guns out of the window, perhaps with the idea of saving themselves by pretending to be hostages. But seconds later, the black-suited SAS troopers burst into the room, identified them and killed them with bursts from their sub-machine guns.

Double-checked

Only one terrorist survived: left to guard the women hostages, he divested himself of weapons and, with the hostages, was searched and swiftly bundled downstairs and into the garden. Except for PC Lock, everyone brought out of the Embassy by the SAS found himself lying face down on the back lawn to be double-checked. The hidden terrorist was unmasked, yanked to his feet and dragged away. In little over 10 minutes, all but one of the hostages had been rescued alive thanks to the incredible speed and efficiency of the SAS.

In a smoke- and flame-filled building there is no time to check on the identities of hostages or terrorists, so anybody who is not fighting is hustled outside at top speed and secured on the ground until they can be identified.

ASSAULT with the SMG

Getting the very best out of a sub-machine gun means knowing exactly what you're doing.

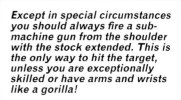

Except in special circumstances you should always fire a sub-machine gun from the shoulder with the stock extended. This is the only way to hit the target, unless you are exceptionally skilled or have arms and wrists like a gorilla!

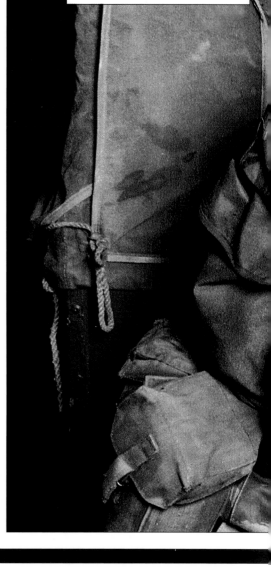

Everyone knows how soldiers fire sub-machine guns. They spray bullets from the hip in long bursts that produce great sheets of muzzle flash. Chuck Norris can even manage one in each hand. Unfortunately, the reality is very different. Using an SMG like this would get its owner killed. Sub-machine guns were the first automatic weapons to weigh about the same as a rifle – and their ability to fire on full auto has remained fixed in film-makers' brains ever since. In fact, unless the target is at very close range, the SMG is fired from the shoulder. It is used rather like a shotgun: keep both eyes open to rapidly acquire targets while concentrating on the foresight.

1 If the target is over 10 metres away, soldiers know they are unlikely to hit it with a burst shot from the hip. They shoulder the SMG and squeeze off an aimed shot.

2 Against targets within 10 metres the SMG is carried in the underarm assault position. It can then be swung toward targets as they appear, hitting them with a short, controlled burst. Long bursts of more than five rounds are usually a waste of ammunition.

3 As they bring the SMG up to fire, well trained troops do not look at the target – they concentrate on their front sight instead.

4 It is vital for soldiers to keep their balance so that they can respond immediately to a new threat at close quarters: it is hard to pivot fast and stay upright with crossed legs!

5 Soldiers look 'through' cover rather than straight at it – they don't expect the enemy to stand up in the open like a target on a range.

6 Experienced men never turn their backs on cover they have not checked out.

7 Corners and windows are treated with great care. Turning sharply around them leaves soldiers no time to react to an enemy lying in wait.

8 Troops do not get any closer than they need to. If they are confident of hitting the target at 10 metres, there is no point getting within arm's reach.

9 Knowledge of malfunction drills is critical. Even the best weapons will have a stoppage from time to time. Stopping to fiddle with the gun in the open is a non-starter – the first priority is to get under cover before sorting out the problem.

10 Even the most experienced soldiers cannot accurately judge how many rounds they have fired in the heat of action. They change magazines after five short bursts to avoid running out of ammunition at the wrong moment.

HANDLING DRILLS

Special Forces troops in counter-revolutionary warfare and hostage rescue units must be masters of their weapons. But the foundation of such skill is good training and the correct application of basic weapons handling.

Normal safety precautions
1 Pick up weapon, ensuring that it is pointing in a safe direction.
2 Set safety catch, keeping finger *outside* trigger guard, well away from trigger.
3 Remove magazine.
4 Roll weapon to one side (so that any cartridge in chamber is not ejected into face); cock weapon, and hold cocking handle to rear. Inspect chamber through ejection port to ensure it is clear.
5 Let bolt forward *under control*. Do not release it; if repeated too often it can damage the bolt head.
6 Set safety, fire off action if necessary, set weapon down.

Load and make ready

1 Soldiers always ensure that the weapon is pointing safely downrange, keeping their finger *outside* the trigger guard.

British technique:

2 Insert loaded magazine. Check magazine is securely engaged.

3 Set safety and cock weapon. **Note:** some SMGs cannot be cocked with the safety on, so set safety after cocking in these cases.

US technique:

2 Pull cocking handle back with left hand, and let forward under control.

3 Lock bolt with safety catch.

4 Insert loaded magazine. Check magazine is securely engaged.

Underarm assault position

1 Only used for close-range combat, under 10 metres.

2 Butt is placed just inside armpit. Both elbows should be hard against body.

3 Soldiers take a stable stance, leaning forward slightly with a pace between feet. They push forward on the weapon with their controlling hand, pulling back with the left hand.

4 The strongest, or master, shooting eye should be directly over axis of barrel.

5 There is a tendency to shoot high from this position, so they aim low.

6 They concentrate on target; watching where the bullets strike and adjusting burst in to target.

Stoppage drill

1 If weapon no longer fires, hit base of magazine hard, recock weapon and fire. This is a combat measure, and should not be done in training.

2 If that does not work, 'cock and look'. Pull back cocking handle and check chamber.

3 If there are no rounds in magazine or chamber, reload.

4 If there is a displaced round or empty case in working parts, tip weapon and shake the obstructing item out.

5 If a live round is stuck in chamber, take out magazine, fire weapon, and replace magazine. Cock and fire.

6 If an empty case has jammed in chamber, throw sub-machine gun at enemy and draw pistol.

Shooting while standing

1 Always shoot with stock extended, which means always carry weapon that way.

2 Always engage safety catch when carrying weapon.

3 Stand with pace between the feet, weight slightly forward. As with a rifle, placing cheek on the stock when firing helps get a better sight picture.

4 Right, or controlling, hand should be as high up pistol grip as is possible and comfortable. The closer the controlling hand is to the axis of the barrel, the more accurate is the shooting.

5 Left hand should always be in the fore end, not gripping magazine. Index finger under barrel pointing towards the target helps with instinctive aiming.

6 Keep hands well away from ejection port and muzzle, especially when firing bursts.

Movement in pairs in buildings

1 Use underarm assault position. Keep well balanced. Do not slide along walls: rubbing noises can give position away to enemies.

2 Do not move along centre of corridors; an enemy will instinctively fire along that axis.

3 Cover and movement is essential. While one man moves the other should always be ready to provide instant covering fire. Clear *every* room along the way. Never pass in front of internal windows: crawl beneath them.

4 Do not go upstairs if you can get up the outside of a building. It is hard to throw grenades accurately upwards, so fight from the top down.

If you have to go upstairs, cover and movement is essential. While one man moves, the other covers any openings or watches the top of the stairwell. Remember, it is much easier for an enemy to roll a grenade down on you than for you to toss one up.

Entering doorways

1 Check from hinges whether door opens inwards or outwards. Team member number one moves to the door while number two covers him. Do *not* stand in front of door; keep to one side.

2 Number one fires a three- to five-round burst through door from kneeling position.

3 Prepare a grenade. Number one pushes door open with base of grenade while number two covers him. As soon as number one can see any of room, he tosses grenade. If number two is able to he also tosses a grenade into opposite corner of room.

4 After grenades explode, assault team enters room fast, one going left and one going right. Short bursts are fired into any enemy in the room, or into cupboards or furniture behind which an enemy could hide. Always shoot low rather than high. When room is clear, one team member covers room while the other covers next entry point. At call 'Room Clear' the next assault team moves through.

Shooting from cover

1 Cover should provide protection from both fire and view: being hidden from sight is not enough if cover will not stop a bullet.

2 Car bodies provide protection from pistol rounds and shotguns, but will not stop rifle bullets. Engine block, wheels and tyres provide additional protection, so fire from behind a wheel. Do not fire from under vehicle, as a shot through the tank could spread burning petrol all over the place.

3 Lying down cuts mobility and speed or reaction: never engage at close range from the prone position.

4 Stand well back from hard cover: too close and near misses could ricochet into the face.

5 When firing from standing position behind cover, rest barrel where left hand would normally be. Left hand should be around magazine.

When using the wheel of a vehicle as cover, remember that an enemy can see under the vehicle. Try to get all of your body behind the wheel, and instead of spreading your legs in the normal prone position, cross one leg over the other.

ASSAULT RIFLES

The rifles used by modern infantrymen are a far cry from those of World War II. Many are capable of automatic fire; some have optical sights as standard. But just how effective are they?

May 1982: British and Argentine troops were fighting yard by yard across the Falkland Islands. It was the traditional rough and tough fighting of infantry battle: men, rifles, grenades; rain and mud. A Royal Marine spotted an Argentine soldier. Aiming his American M16 rifle, he shot four rounds into the Argentine. Incredibly, the soldier was not disabled. Undeterred, he fired back with his FN FAL rifle and seriously wounded the Marine. Had the weapons been reversed, the Argentine would probably never have survived the first round.

Assault rifles are at the very sharpest end of battle. Once the fighters, bombers, ships, artillery and tanks have done their business, the ground has to be won by the individual infantryman, simply equipped with his personal weapon, the rifle. So what makes a good assault rifle?

Compromise design

Modern assault rifles have to meet several conflicting requirements. Since most soldiers ride into battle in cramped armoured personnel carriers (APCs), their rifles must be relatively short. Yet they must be able to hit and kill the enemy at up to about 500 metres: and that demands a reasonably powerful cartridge and a fairly long barrel. But most modern rifles are also capable of fully automatic fire, so weapon designers have to strike a balance between a powerful but heavy cartridge and a lighter one that will enable the soldier to carry more bullets.

The FN FAL used by the Argentines fires a bullet that measures 7.62-mm in cross-section (known technically as its calibre), weighs 9.3 grammes, and travels at 822 metres per second. The M16 fires a smaller 5.56-mm calibre bullet at 1,000 metres per second; but it only weighs 3.56 grammes. The lighter bul-

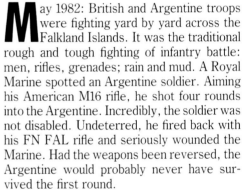

5.56-mm cases fly into the air as a Lebanese soldier fires his M16 rifle at Druze militiamen during 1983. The M16 was introduced by the US Army in the 1960s and most major armies have now introduced 5.56-mm weapons themselves.

Modern Rifle Bullets (Life Size)

British .303-in
Bullet weight: 11.27 grammes; velocity: 731 metres per second

The .303 bullet used in both world wars was so powerful that in 1914 British troops could open effective fire at over 1,000 metres.

NATO 7.62-mm
Bullet weight: 9.3 grammes; velocity: 838 metres per second

Fired by the FN FAL and G3, this bullet was adopted by NATO under pressure from the USA. It is not much lighter than the old .303 and is too powerful for automatic fire.

Soviet 7.62-mm
Bullet weight: 7.91 grammes; velocity: 710 metres per second

Fired by the AK-47 and AKM, this bullet first appeared in 1943. It is very similar to the shortened 7.92-mm round introduced by the Germans a year earlier.

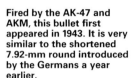

American 5.56-mm
Bullet weight: 3.56 grammes; velocity: 1,005 metres per second

Fired by the M16, this type of round has become the new standard NATO bullet. It allows soldiers to carry much more ammunition.

Soviet 5.45-mm
Bullet weight: 3.4 grammes; velocity: 900 metres per second

The Soviet answer to NATO 5.56-mm, this is designed to extract the most effect from a very light round. It tumbles on impact, inflicting devastating wounds.

Above: The standard magazine fitted to the British SLR contained 20 7.62-mm rounds, loaded from five-round stripper clips. But 40-round magazines are now available for the M16: twice the magazine capacity!

let is widely acknowledged as less effective: but despite this, most armies now use it as their standard rifle cartridge.

This is not as illogical as it may seem. Soldiers can carry far more of the lighter bullets: Australian SAS troopers in Vietnam each had 300 rounds for their M16s. But British soldiers equipped with their own version of the FN FAL, the Self Loading Rifle (SLR), were issued with only 100 rounds. While the lighter round is less powerful, it is still perfectly capable of inflicting dreadful injuries, and armies are willing to trade a little performance for the increased ammunition supply. Firing 5.56-mm bullets is also softer on the firer's shoulder, which makes recruits less likely to flinch and makes accurate shooting easier to teach. So, as is often the case, it is a trade-off: injury-inflicting calibre, ammunition supply, range and accuracy.

The dramatic name 'assault rifle' was first applied by Adolf Hitler. He included a new rifle in his list of 'wonder weapons' which he announced to the German people in 1944. The gun he referred to was certainly a wonder, but not enough to turn the tide. The *Sturmgewehr 44* created the distinctive shape of the modern rifle, complete with pistol grip and banana-shaped magazine. It was developed to solve a problem that had become obvious during World War I.

Early 1900s weapons

The rifles in service at the beginning of this century were single-shot weapons, reloaded by pulling back a bolt on the side. This chambered another round from a five- to 10-round magazine. 'Rapid' fire was possible: the Germans were astonished at the volume of British fire in 1914. The long-service volunteers of the British Expeditionary Force could manage 25 aimed shots a minute (compared with a modern auto rate of 200 rounds per minute), but this took time to learn – time that conscript armies did not have. These bolt-

ASSAULT RIFLE Reference File

23 USA
M16 5.56-mm rifle

Developed during the late 1950s, the M16 was bought by the US Air Force for its guards defending bases in Vietnam. Its light weight and handiness recommended the rifle to the small-statured South Vietnamese. When the US Army's own experimental weapons test programme failed it turned to the M16, which was soon delivered to the rapidly expanding Army and Marine forces in South East Asia.

Introduced as a 'self-cleaning rifle' the M16 made a poor impression as it entered widespread service. In fact, since the gas produced on firing works directly on the bolt, the M16 requires rather more care than the Soviet Kalashnikov series. The problem stemmed from an unannounced

Right: The M16 is light, easy to handle and a delight to shoot. After initial problems, it proved highly reliable in Vietnam.

change in the cartridge propellant, and sloppy practice among some units. Once this was ironed out, the M16 did very well indeed. Although lightly built, it proved tough enough in the field and was soon adopted by many other armies.

The current production model, the M16A2, is easily distinguished by its ribbed foregrip. The ability to fire fully automatic has been replaced by a three-round burst facility since longer bursts are more of a danger to low flying aircraft than enemy soldiers.

Specification
M16A1 5.56-mm rifle
Calibre: 5.56mm×45
Weight: 3.82kg with 30-round magazine and sling fitted
Length: 990mm
Barrel length: 508mm

Muzzle velocity: 1000 metres per second
Cyclic rate of fire: 700-950 rounds per minute
Magazine capacity: 20- or 30-rounds
Users: USA, Great Britain, Korea and many South American forces

Above: A classic image of the Vietnam war – US paratroops engage Viet Cong guerrillas with M16 rifles.

Right: The SA80, adopted by the British Army in 1988, has now seen action in Northern Ireland, where it has performed very well.

action rifles fired bullets from long-barrelled weapons and had a very long range: in 1898 the British infantry at Omdurman opened fire on the Sudanese at well over 1,000 metres. But dense masses of spearmen did not re-appear as targets during World War I. Instead, soldiers found themselves in trenches, 200 metres apart, and armed with a rifle which was too long and unnecessarily powerful.

Most soldiers fought World War II with the same rifles. Few nations spent much on their armies in the 1920s and 1930s. When they did, aircraft and tanks were the priority: infantry-men could make do with the millions of existing rifles left over from the previous war. Hitler saw no need to worry about rifles, and the German 'assault rifle' was actually developed against his orders – its designers classified it as a sub-machine gun to disguise it when they supplied 8,000 of them to units

fighting the Russians on the Eastern Front. They were very successful; so Hitler changed his mind, and over 400,000 *Sturmgewehr* 44s were built by the end of the war.

Hitler's 'assault rifle' made a big impression on the Soviets who were already working along similar lines, introducing a shorter, lighter 7.62-mm bullet in 1944. Several rifles were developed to fire it, and the one selected for the Soviet army after the war became the most famous assault rifle of them all: the AK-47.

The Red Army rifleman had frequently ridden into battle on top of a T-34 tank ready to dismount and assault German positions as the armour swept through. Now he rode into action in a new generation of armoured personnel carriers. With the introduction of the BMP infantry fighting vehicle in the late 1960s, he no longer had to dismount to shoot.

24

SA80 5.56-mm rifle

UNITED KINGDOM

The SA80 is the current British service rifle, though Special Forces units prefer the US M16A2 and during the Gulf War some troops even returned to using the old SLR because of its long-range killing power. The 'bullpup' layout – placing the magazine behind the trigger group – allows the SA80 to have a relatively long barrel while reducing the overall length of the weapon. The optical sight is a great aid to good shooting, especially in low-light conditions. Most units equipped with the rifle have noted a sharp increase in accuracy on the firing range.

Fifteen years after entering service, the SA80 continues to be controversial. Formidably accurate and a delight to shoot, it has been dogged by problems. The magazines tended to drop out, the

Right: The optical sight on the SA80 makes it extremely accurate. This is especially important in poor light conditions, when iron sights merge with an indistinct target, making it difficult to aim.

optical sights fog up and the foregrips break. These and other teething problems would have been understandable in a weapon rushed into action, but the SA80 was introduced after a protracted and expensive development programme. Time will iron out the bugs, no doubt, but a lot of money has been wasted and no foreign army is likely to buy it.

Specification
SA80 5.56-mm rifle
Calibre: 5.56mm×45
Weight: 4.98kg with 30-round magazine
Length: 785mm

Barrel length: 518mm
Muzzle velocity: 940m/s
Cyclic rate of fire: 650-800 rounds per minute
Magazine capacity: 30
User: British Army

Ports were provided in the side of the vehicle and all the riflemen had to do was to point their AKs through and add to the volume of automatic fire provided by·the vehicle's machine-gun and cannon armament.

In the West, the post-war rifle developed along similar lines for much the same reasons.

Above: The British SA80 can only be fired from the right shoulder: shooting it from the left would cause it to eject its empty cases into the soldier's ear. This SA80 lacks the optical sight, so the soldier is aiming with the back-up iron sights.

How Bullets Kill

Despite intensive research throughout this century, there is no hard and fast formula for predicting the lethality of a particular type of round. Bullets inflict injury in three ways:

1 The bullet destroys everything in its path through the body.
2 The impact creates a 'temporary cavity' for a fraction of a second. This violent distortion causes more damage.
3 Bullets sometimes break up or shatter bone, producing a hail of secondary missiles that inflict wound tracks of their own.

Below: The diagram shows the distinctive shape of a wound caused by a Soviet 5.45-mm bullet as it tumbles through a body.

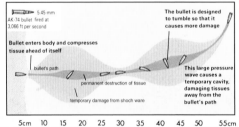

5.45-mm
AK-74 bullet fired at
3,066 ft per second

The bullet is designed to tumble so that it causes more damage

Bullet enters body and compresses tissue ahead of itself

bullet's path

This large pressure wave causes a temporary cavity, damaging tissues away from the bullet's path

permanent destruction of tissue

temporary damage from shock ware

5cm 10 15 20 25 30 35 40 45 50 55cm

The heart and lungs of a deer shot with a 7.62-mm round. An unfired 7.62-mm round contrasts with the now mushroomed hunting round that caused the damage.

25

FRANCE

FA MAS 5.56-mm rifle

The French army was among the first military forces to adopt a 'bullpup' rifle. Capable of single-shot, three-round burst or fully automatic fire, the FA MAS is unusual in having a permanently attached bipod. Whereas the British SA80 cannot be fired by a left-handed shot – it will eject empty cases into the shooter's ear – the FA MAS can be switched over to eject its cases on either side. The process is quite straightforward, although not recommended in action where small parts might be lost.

The 25-round magazines have small holes drilled in them at five-round intervals to give the firer a rough idea of his remaining ammunition supply. The standard FA MAS is capable of

Right: The FA MAS can be adjusted to eject its empty cases to either side, so left-handed soldiers do not have a problem. The fold-down bipod is fitted as standard.

launching rifle grenades, but an 'Export model' has been produced – this cannot fire them and is only capable of single shots. A civilian model chambered for .222 Remington is also manufactured. This odd choice of calibre is dictated by French firearms law, which restricts the use of military calibres by civilian shooters.

Specification
FA MAS 5.56-mm rifle
Calibre: 5.56mm×45
Weight: 3.61kg empty
Length: 757mm
Barrel length: 488mm
Muzzle velocity: 960m/s

Cyclic rate of fire: 900-1000 rounds per minute
Magazine capacity: 25 rounds
Users: France, Senegal, Djibouti and the UAE. Saw service in Chad against Libyan forces and their allies

---

26

GERMANY

Heckler & Koch G3 7.62-mm rifle

The wartime German designers who escaped to Spain after World War II built on their earlier assault rifle designs to produce the CETME series of rifles. In turn, the first CETME rifle was developed by an intermediary and was adopted by the newly-formed West German army. Further development and production was taken over by Heckler & Koch and Germany was back in the assault rifle business.

The G3 has been adopted all over the world, and its popularity ensures that it will remain in service for many years to come. Ballistics research has shown that the West German 7.62-mm round is even more effective than standard NATO 7.62-mm: it tends to fracture on impact, causing more serious wounds

Right: The G3 is one of the classic 7.62-mm rifles that are now being replaced by 5.56-mm weapons in NATO armies. German 7.62-mm ammunition is the most effective in military service.

and a greater chance of immediate incapacitation.

The basic system of the G3 has been used for 5.56-mm rifles and even modified for the famous MP5 series sub-machine guns. Cut-down 7.62-mm assault rifle variants and the heavyweight PSG-1 sniper rifle complete the series.

Specification
G3 7.62-mm rifle
Calibre: 7.62mm×51
Weight: 4.4kg empty
Length: 1025mm
Barrel length: 450mm
Muzzle velocity: 800m/s

Cyclic rate of fire: 500-600 rounds per minute
Magazine capacity: 20 rounds
Users: Germany and at least 48 other countries. Thirteen countries manufacture the G3 under licence

The US Army, which had had the distinction of being the first to adopt a self-loading rifle, the M1 Garand, modified its wartime rifle to produce the M14. American pressure led the NATO armies to choose a more powerful round than the wartime German and Soviet cartridges. Like the Soviets, NATO adopted a 7.62-mm calibre cartridge: but it is slightly heavier and sits in a longer case containing almost twice as much powder. This makes it harder-hitting and more accurate at over 300 metres.

Off to Spain

Members of the team which developed the German *Sturmgewehr* 44 fled to Spain after the war and designed a new rifle, which soon entered service with their adopted nation. A modified version of this soon appeared in the Army. This was designated the G3 and it went on to be a true world-beater, arming the German Army and nearly 50 other armies worldwide.

But the most successful 7.62-mm NATO assault rifle was the FN FAL, produced by the Belgian company, Fabrique Nationale. The British Army was one of over 70 armies to adopt it. Britain eventually manufactured its own version, the Self Loading Rifle (SLR), modified to prevent fully automatic fire – with such a powerful round, the rifle is difficult to control on automatic.

The new round and the rifles to fire it were barely in service before the Americans unilaterally adopted a smaller-calibre weapon instead. The Armalite AR-15 5.56-mm calibre rifle was supplied to US Air Force personnel in the expanding war in Vietnam. It was instantly popular, and ideal for the small-statured South Vietnamese too. The US Army was impressed and took it into service in time for the major battles of the Vietnam War. Adopted under the designation M16, it became the enduring symbol of the US infantryman in South East Asia.

The idea of the rifleman firing his rifle from an APC and effectively becoming a vehicle crewman did not prove successful in the 1973 Arab-Israeli war. Despite the development of increasingly powerful infantry fighting vehicles (IFVs), infantrymen still have to dismount to capture enemy positions with close-range rifle shooting, so several armies have adopted a 'bullpup' design for their rifles. By placing the magazine behind the pistol grip, the overall length of the weapon can be dra-

Right: The camera catches the muzzle flash of an SA80. True gun flashes only last for a fraction of a second; a camera will see it, but a human eye will not.

27
BELGIUM
FN FAL

Adopted by the British Army as the SLR (Self Loading Rifle), the FN is the most successful Western rifle since World War II. In service all over the world by the early 1960s, it is tough, reliable and hard-hitting. Although it raised a few eyebrows among traditionalists at first, its replacement in British service is now lamented by devotees of the bigger calibre. So many armies use the FN that it has often been used by both sides in a battle: the most recent example is the Falklands war where the British SLR faced fully automatic versions in Argentine hands.

Although production in Belgium finished in 1987, the FN FAL will be seen for many years to come because it is in such widespread service. In

Right: This early model FAL (above) has wooden furniture and no flash hider. The Argentine FAL (below) has a folding stock. The latter was captured in the Falklands and used against its former owners.

addition to the standard rifle, it is also seen in heavy-barrel and folding-stock versions: both were prized souvenirs from the Falklands. Some British troops even used captured Argentine FN FALs: their fully automatic fire capability was handy at point-blank range.

Specification
FN FAL
Calibre: 7.62 mm × 51
Weight: 5 kg with loaded magazine
Length: 1090 mm
Barrel length: 533 mm
Muzzle velocity: 840 m/s

Cyclic rate of fire: 650-700 rounds per minute
Magazine capacity: 20 rounds
Users: Belgium and over 50 countries. Manufactured in Argentina, Australia, Belgium, Britain, Canada, India, Israel, Nigeria and South Africa

28
USSR
AK-74 5.45-mm rifle

This is the latest version of the famous Kalashnikov rifle. Firing a new, lighter cartridge that is cleverly designed to produce fearsome wounds, the AK-74 is as superb a weapon as its predecessors. Effective to normal battlefield ranges, it is simply built and easy to understand. By following such an evolutionary development, the Soviets greatly simplify the training of their reserves. Anyone trained on the AK-47, even years ago, will have no trouble mastering the AK-74. In the same time, British soldiers have had the bolt-action Lee-Enfield, the SLR and now the SA80: three totally different weapons.

The AK-74 performed successfully in Afghanistan, where light machine-gun and cut-down carbine versions were also encountered. A unique muzzle brake makes it the best controlled rifle when using fully automatic fire. Its only disadvantage is a fearsome sideways blast that can deafen someone next to the firer. On the other hand, the negligible recoil makes it very easy to shoot.

The AK-74 continues the Kalashnikov tradition of simple, tough rifles that do not tax the brain of the average conscript. Accurate enough at battle ranges, it fires a bullet specially designed to produce maximum injury.

Specification
AK-74 5.45-mm rifle
Calibre: 5.45 mm × 39
Weight: 3.6 kg unloaded
Length: 930 mm
Barrel length: 400 mm

Muzzle velocity: 900 m/s
Cyclic rate of fire: 650 rounds per minute
Magazine capacity: 30 rounds
Users: Soviet Union, Hungary and other Warsaw Pact forces

matically reduced. This makes weapons like the British SA80 or French FA MAS far more suitable for cramped vehicle interiors.

The modern rifle is the product of several conflicting requirements. It must be simple to use so that riflemen do not require prolonged training. It must be as compact as possible, and tough enough to keep working in muddy or sandy conditions. It must fire a round small enough to enable the soldier to carry a lot of them, but sufficiently powerful to inflict crippling injury.

The Austrian Steyr AUG rifle pioneered the use of a low-power optical scope to improve accuracy. The AK-74 has a unique muzzle brake to make automatic fire more controllable. The French FA MAS has an integral bipod to provide the rifleman with a steady support at a moment's notice. But the differences between modern rifles are more due to national preferences than practical advantages. The margin of superiority enjoyed by the best weapons is very slim compared with the one factor common to them all: the rifleman holding it.

Left: The Austrian Steyr AUG has been adopted by the Australian army. It is one of the best assault rifles in production.

Below: Since most infantry ride into action in APCs, their rifles must be shorter and handier than the weapons of World War II.

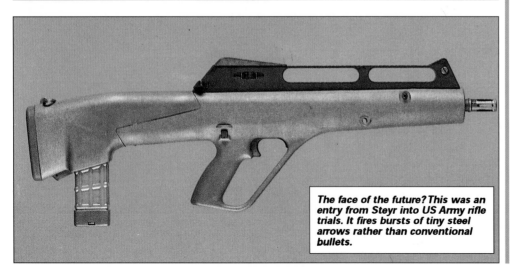

The face of the future? This was an entry from Steyr into US Army rifle trials. It fires bursts of tiny steel arrows rather than conventional bullets.

How ASSAULT

1907 British .303 SMLE

1944 German 7.92-mm Sturmgewehr 44

1959 Soviet 7.62-mm AKM

1980 French 5.56-mm FA MAS

Right: By placing the magazine behind the trigger group, it is possible to have a relatively long barrel in a smaller weapon. The FA MAS has a longer barrel than the AK, which increases its accuracy, but the rifle is over 15cm shorter.

RIFLES developed

In 1939 European armies went to war with much the same rifles they had used in World War I. They were designed for shooting at 1000 metres' range — although few targets were ever engaged at over 400 metres. During World War II, the Germans introduced a very different sort of rifle: the StG 44, which set the pattern for modern rifles. The rifles illustrated here are all to a constant scale.

Below: In 1914, British soldiers armed with the SMLE (Short, Magazine, Lee-Enfield) rifle astonished their German opponents with a rate of fire of between 15 and 25 aimed rounds per minute. A self-loading rifle allows a soldier to at least double this.

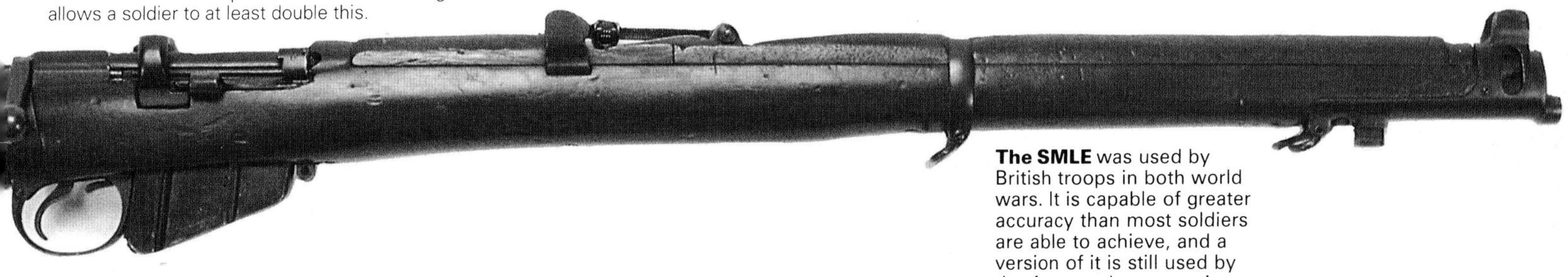

The SMLE was used by British troops in both world wars. It is capable of greater accuracy than most soldiers are able to achieve, and a version of it is still used by the Army today as a sniper rifle.

Above: The name 'assault rifle' has been applied to most post-war rifles. It was coined by the Germans to describe this revolutionary weapon, which was first introduced against Hitler's orders. Firing a shortened version of the German 7.92-mm cartridge, it was capable of fully automatic fire and accurate enough at battlefield ranges.

The Sturmgewehr gave German infantry a big advantage over troops armed with bolt-action weapons like the SMLE. Fortunately for the Allies, only a third of the 525,000 weapons produced actually reached the front line.

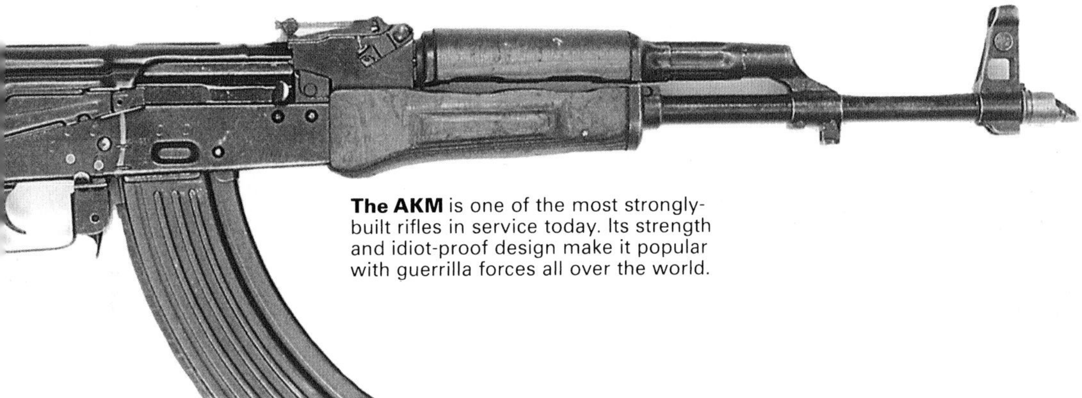

The AKM is one of the most strongly-built rifles in service today. Its strength and idiot-proof design make it popular with guerrilla forces all over the world.

Left : The AKM was a development of the AK-47, which the Soviets introduced after World War II. The appearance of this short rifle, capable of automatic fire, made the sub-machine gun obsolete as a military weapon. It is the most widely manufactured rifle in history, with an estimated 50 million built in the last 40 years.

The FA MAS has a permanently attached bipod that can be swung down to provide a stable platform for deliberate shooting. Its 'bullpup' design makes it the shortest military rifle in service.

The AK

Rough, Tough and Ready

Above: Soviet infantry fight from armoured personnel carriers: they dismount several hundred metres from the enemy position and skirmish forward. Here a rifleman covers a soldier armed with an RPG-7 anti-tank rocket launcher.

Left: Another AK version: the AKSU-74. Seen here at the Soviet airborne training school at Ryazan, it is just 420mm long with the butt folded. It fires the 5.45-mm cartridge and is designed for airborne troops, special forces and tank crew.

For 40 years the Soviet infantry has been armed with the AK series of rifles. They are sturdy, reliable and idiot-proof, and are ideally suited to Soviet infantry tactics.

Russian infantrymen do not march to battle. They fight from the back of armoured vehicles as powerful as some of the tanks used in WWII. The bulk of their firepower no longer comes from the rifles of the foot soldiers. The famous Kalashnikov rifle is simply one element in the deadly array of weapons deployed by a combined arms team.

The Russians rely heavily on their powerful artillery to soften up the enemy – attaching many more guns and rocket launchers to their formations than NATO armies. In attack or defence, the Russian soldier is closely supported by the machine-gun and cannon armament of his armoured personnel carrier and the immense power of the tanks that are part of every Motor Rifle Regiment.

Russian weapons are much more carefully tailored to the abilities of the soldier using them than many Western ones. The classic AK series of rifles is simple to maintain and operate. The rifles tend to look rather tacky alongside Western infantry weapons, but their strength is incredible.

Indestructible AK

For example, an English civilian shooter who had to surrender his AK-47 under the Firearms Act of 1988 decided to destroy it first. The AK was loaded, the barrel filled with earth and the rifle hammered into the ground. It was remotely fired via a piece of string tied to the trigger. The 40-year-old rifle blew itself free from the ground, having cleared its barrel without any damage. It went on to repeat this performance several times and eventually had to be sawn up. Few, if any, other rifles could match this incredible strength and reliability. Whether in the Arctic wastes of Siberia, the African bush or the jungles of Vietnam, the AK's reliability is outstanding.

The Russian infantryman is not expected to kill his opponents with carefully aimed shots at long range, so his rifle does not have to be highly accurate. Depending on the lie of the land and the tactical situation, the infantry dismount from their BMPs to assault the enemy between 200 and 400 metres from their objective and fight their way forward. They advance under covering fire of the BMPs and tanks, relying more on the volume of their fire rather than individual accuracy. Although the rifleman's AKs will not perform well over 400 metres, longer range shooting is not their job. Any targets at greater distances will be engaged with the section's two machine-guns: usually heavily barreled versions of the rifle, fitted with a bipod and larger magazines. Enemy officers or tank commanders, incautiously sitting up in their turrets, are targets for the platoon sniper.

There is little tactical finesse here: Russian minor tactics generally consist of set-piece drills. Apart from small units of Special Forces, the Russian military does not concern itself with small units. Where the British Army tends to use platoons and companies as semi-independent units, the Russians rarely deploy anything smaller than a battalion on a single task. Their tactics may lack flexibility, but at least they are simple to teach to ill-educated conscripts – and relatively easy to remember in the stress of action.

Reliable weapon

In the close-quarter battle that follows, it is better to have a weapon that can be relied on, even when covered in mud, than a rifle that is accurate to 1000 metres but needs careful maintenance. In the last resort, all Russian rifles work well as clubs or spears. US Marines who fought hand-to-hand against North Vietnamese in Hue city complained that the plastic stocks of

their M16s tended to snap off.

The Russian infantryman is part of a colossal armed fighting machine. His arrival on an enemy position is the last stage of a combined arms assault, finishing off an opponent already pounded by artillery, rockets, aircraft, helicopters and tanks. His weapons are strictly functional tools designed for this very specific job. It is this emphasis on reliability and basic simplicity that has made Soviet rifles and machine-guns enormously popular with armies and guerrilla forces throughout the world.

73-mm cannon
Firing low-velocity rounds to a range of 8 metres, this has been replaced by a 30-mm cannon on later version. The 'Sagger' missiles a now being swapped fc a copy of the NATO MILAN system.

Front armour
Sloped at 80 degrees, the BMP's 8-mm armour will keep out rifle and machine gun fire, but not 20-mm cannon or anything heavier. The vehicle is crammed with fuel and ammunition and explodes with deadly effect if penetrated.

Selector

The position of the long bar above the trigger sets the AK to fire single shots when pushed fully down. In the middle position, the AK will fire fully automatic at a cyclic rate of 650rpm. On its top setting it locks the trigger and acts as a safety by preventing the bolt from coming all the way back. The firer can still pull back the cocking handle to see if there is a round in the chamber.

Bolt system

The AK bolt system is the heart of the gun's legendary reliability. Locking – the process in which a bolt is firmly held in place against the cartridge before firing – is done by means of rotating two lugs on the bolt into recesses on the receiver wall. The rotating-bolt system is used by most modern assault rifles, but the AK has a much greater rotation and larger lugs than normal, and thus has a more solid and dependable action.

Improved accuracy

The AKM had a rate-reducer (a cable applying a fractional restraint on the hammer after the trigger has been pulled) fitted, which gave it a slower rate of fire than the original AK-47. Rate-of-fire on the AK-47 is about 750rpm, while on the AKM it is closer to 650rpm. The aim of this change was to improve accuracy, and to that end an angular compensator was added at the muzzle to counteract the climb of the AKM when on full auto.

AKM Assault Rifle

The AK-47 started the most prolific series of weapons ever produced. If we include all the international variants, up to 80 million AKs have been produced and distributed, and the illegal trade in AKs worldwide is one of the biggest contemporary security issues. Perhaps the most prolific AK variant is the AKM. The 'M' stands for 'Modernized', and was Kalashnikov's successful attempt in the 1950s to make a cheaper and even more resilient weapon.

Stock

AKMs have been manufactured internationally in numerous different versions. Many are fitted with collapsible metal stocks instead of the fixed laminated wood versions. This saves room – important in a vehicle or for airborne troops; but folding stocks tend to wobble after a while, making accurate shooting more difficult. Some Eastern European versions of the AKM have plastic stocks and foregrips. Even the wooden ones vary in appearance from dark colours to very loud plywood finishes.

Far left: During World War II the Soviet infantry rode into action on top of their tanks. Here they dismount from a T-55 in a 1960s exercise.

Left: This Soviet paratrooper is armed with the 5.45-mm AK-74, which is now standard issue to first-line formations. He wears their new camouflage uniform and the distinctive striped T-shirt of Soviet airborne forces.

Right: Soviet infantry weapons are not designed to be used on their own: the infantry fight with close support of their APCs and the tanks attached to every infantry regiment.

The Soviet Infantry Platoon

A Soviet infantry platoon consists of three rifle sections, each riding in an armoured personnel carrier. A section normally comprises a driver and gunner for the BMP armoured personnel carrier, the section commander and eight men in the troop compartment. The exact organisation and armament varies according to the readiness of the unit. Although the bulk of the troops are armed with rifles, there are several important specialists. The eight troops who dismount to fight with the section commander include one man with an RPG anti-tank rocket launcher, two machine-gunners with bipod-mounted light machine-guns, and one other soldier. In one of the sections he is another ordinary rifleman; in another he carries an SA-7 shoulder-fired anti-aircraft missile; the third is the platoon sniper, armed with an SVD 'Dragunov' 7.62-mm sniper rifle.

BMP Infantry Assault Vehicle

Soviet infantry ride into battle in BMP assault vehicles, which saw their first real action in the 1973 Arab-Israeli war. This is a Syrian BMP-1 armed with 73-mm cannon and 'Sagger' anti-tank missiles.

Firing ports
The infantry can fire their AKs through these openings in the side. They aim through periscopes above them. Unfortunately this fills the troop compartment with choking fumes, and covers the floor with spent cases. The vacuum hoses that are supposed to clear the air are not very effective.

Commander
He is the section, platoon or company commander, and dismounts with the infantry in the back.

Gunner
When the commander leaves the vehicle with the infantry, the gunner directs the BMP. It is a tough job because he must also fire the cannon.

Driver mechanic
The Soviet equivalent of a lance-corporal, he has six months' specialist training.

GUNS
FOR THE
GUERRILLAS

"Power grows out of the barrel of a gun," according to Mao Tse Tung, and the gun that is most used is the AK-47. It's rough and ready but it can be used to deadly effect by peasant guerrillas, urban terrorists, radical freedom fighters and drug runners the world over.

Nicaragua
The communist regime in Nicaragua confidently expected to win the February election. But President Ortega and his supporters (including Mr Neil Kinnock, chairman of the Nicaraguan solidarity campaign) were astonished when the voters decisively rejected them. The Contras' guerrilla war is now over

Despite the radical changes in Europe and Russia, world peace has not broken out. There are nearly 30 full-scale conflicts going on today, ranging from civil wars to armed resistance against a foreign invader. Perhaps the most notorious civil war recently took place in Yugoslavia, but for many the defining period of world terrorism and guerrilla war was that of the 1980s.

At this time the classic left-wing guerrilla struggles against American-backed governments continued in Latin America. But with the collapse of the Sandanistas in Nicaragua and the Soviets' loss of interest, forces like the FMLN in El Salvador started to wither on the vine. By the same token, guerrilla armies fighting communist regimes took fresh heart: the Marxist governments in Angola, Ethiopia and Cambodia looked unlikely to survive.

The acquisition of new weapon types meant that the world could no longer dismiss these wars as local conflicts. Iraq had been using poison in its war against the Kurds. Others, including Colonel Gaddafi's Libya, were trying to acquire nuclear weapons. Preparing for war seemed to remain the wisest policy, especially for those who desired peace.

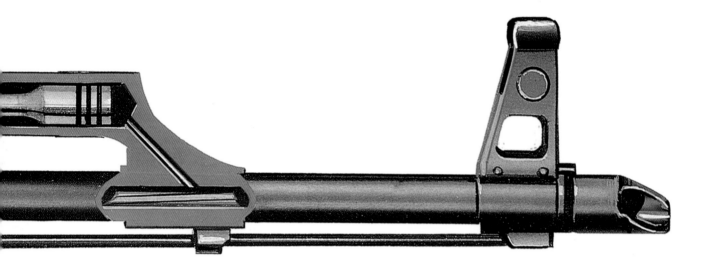

Gas operation
When the bullet passes the gas-tube junction just a few inches behind the barrel, some of its propellant gases are diverted into the tube above. This contains a spring-loaded piston which cycles back and forth under pressure from the gas and via the bolt's resistance against the recoil spring, keeping the weapon firing while the trigger is held back. The AKM's rate-of-fire is around 650rpm.

Rear Sight

The rear sight of an AKM is adjustable up to 800m (2624ft) – a very optimistic distance at which to shoot someone with an AK. The path of the bullet is affected by the wind and it can be deflected by striking relatively light vegetation. This being said, at up to 200m (656ft) the AKM is a truly lethal firearm as it can empty its 30-round magazine in a matter of seconds.

30-round magazine

In Vietnam, the North Vietnamese troops equipped with AKs enjoyed one advantage over their American opponents: the US M16 was only issued with a 20-round magazine. Soviet magazines also tended to be much more solidly built than US ones – this makes them heavier, but less likely to get dented and cause a malfunction in the heat of battle. AKM magazines come in sheet metal and orange-red plastic versions.

AK-47: The Guerrilla's Choice

The AK-47 has been around for over half a century, churned out at a rate of about one million every year. It's the guerrilla's choice for all the right reasons. Almost completely idiot-proof, it can be dropped in the mud and can fire thousands of rounds without the need for cleaning. It can be easily maintained; spare parts are a dime a dozen; and almost anyone — even someone without any weapon-training — can be taught to fire it.

Reliability
Guerrillas like the AK because Kalashnikov's relatively simple design means that even poorly maintained examples can be relied on to fire.

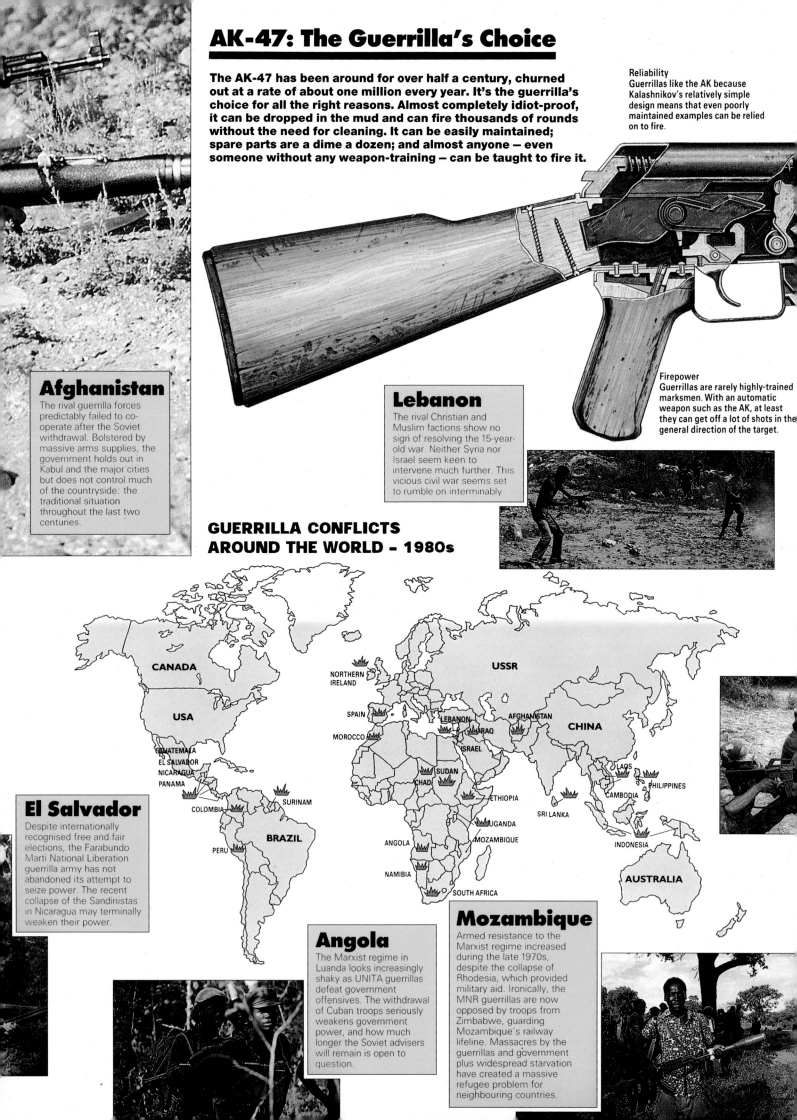

Firepower
Guerrillas are rarely highly-trained marksmen. With an automatic weapon such as the AK, at least they can get off a lot of shots in the general direction of the target.

Afghanistan
The rival guerrilla forces predictably failed to co-operate after the Soviet withdrawal. Bolstered by massive arms supplies, the government holds out in Kabul and the major cities but does not control much of the countryside: the traditional situation throughout the last two centuries.

Lebanon
The rival Christian and Muslim factions show no sign of resolving the 15-year-old war. Neither Syria nor Israel seem keen to intervene much further. This vicious civil war seems set to rumble on interminably.

GUERRILLA CONFLICTS AROUND THE WORLD – 1980s

CANADA
USA
GUATEMALA
EL SALVADOR
NICARAGUA
PANAMA
COLOMBIA
SURINAM
PERU
BRAZIL
NORTHERN IRELAND
SPAIN
MOROCCO
LEBANON
ISRAEL
IRAQ
SUDAN
CHAD
ETHIOPIA
UGANDA
ANGOLA
MOZAMBIQUE
NAMIBIA
SOUTH AFRICA
USSR
AFGHANISTAN
CHINA
LAOS
CAMBODIA
PHILIPPINES
SRI LANKA
INDONESIA
AUSTRALIA

El Salvador
Despite internationally recognised free and fair elections, the Farabundo Marti National Liberation guerrilla army has not abandoned its attempt to seize power. The recent collapse of the Sandinistas in Nicaragua may terminally weaken their power.

Angola
The Marxist regime in Luanda looks increasingly shaky as UNITA guerrillas defeat government offensives. The withdrawal of Cuban troops seriously weakens government power, and how much longer the Soviet advisers will remain is open to question.

Mozambique
Armed resistance to the Marxist regime increased during the late 1970s, despite the collapse of Rhodesia, which provided military aid. Ironically, the MNR guerrillas are now opposed by troops from Zimbabwe, guarding Mozambique's railway lifeline. Massacres by the guerrillas and government plus widespread starvation have created a massive refugee problem for neighbouring countries.

aintenance
th so many rifles in circulation, are parts for the AK are no problem. d if you break the butt, just carve urself another and screw it on.

In action
By some standards, the Kalashnikov does not have a long range. But at 400 metres or less a partly trained guerrilla is more likely to hit the target with an AK than with the latest high-tech sniper rifle, which requires thorough training to make the best use of its capabilities.

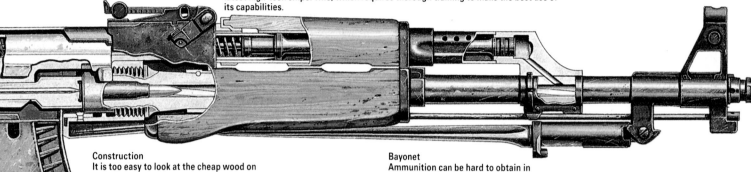

Construction
It is too easy to look at the cheap wood on the AK and assume that it is a shoddy piece of work. In fact it is very well made, which explains its ability to take rough handling.

Bayonet
Ammunition can be hard to obtain in the bush, so when you run out of bullets and your rifle becomes a club, a bayonet is a handy tool for changing it into a spear.

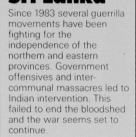

Philippines

he late, unlamented resident Marcos failed to vercome a powerful ommunist guerrilla novement, which is now aging war against Mrs quino's government. As elements of the army have been involved in failed coups, increasing its share of the budget may not be a top priority for the current regime. On Mindanao, Muslim guerrillas are also fighting for independence.

Sri Lanka

Since 1983 several guerrilla movements have been fighting for the independence of the northern and eastern provinces. Government offensives and inter-communal massacres led to Indian intervention. This failed to end the bloodshed and the war seems set to continue.

Cambodia

The withdrawal of Vietnamese forces leaves the Cambodian government fighting a coalition of guerrilla movements, including the barbarous Khmer Rouge. Still under the same leadership responsible for the 'Killing Fields', the Khmer Rouge may yet return to power.

Guatemala

Latin America's least effective army continues to grapple with left-wing guerrillas in a very low intensity war. Guatemala has never dropped its claim to neighbouring Belize, so British troops are still stationed there to discourage any thoughts of invasion.

Colombia

Colombian governments, both military and civilian, have been opposed by various left-wing guerrilla movements since the mid-1960s. But this war has now taken second place to the struggle against the drug barons. With enough cash to pay the country's awesome international debt, the cocaine kings continue to defy Bogota and Washington alike.

Peru

In 1980 the Sendero Luminoso ('Shining Path') guerrillas began a war that has become infamously cruel even by Latin American standards. The embattled government has made little major headway, although reforms of the police and army are improving its military strength.

Panama

The US military intervention in Panama has removed the notorious General Noriega to an American courtroom where he will fight his final battle. Until the local police and army units can be reorganised, US forces remain responsible for security in Panama.

Surinam

This tiny country (pop: 400,000; area: 63,000 square miles) was part of the Netherlands West Indies until 1975. During the 1980s the government has been opposed by a guerrilla movement assisted by small numbers of French, British and other mercenaries.

Northern Ireland

Republican terrorism continues to claim lives both sides of the water, and on the continent, where British army personnel are again under attack. The British government continues to pour money into the province, hoping to undermine the basis of Republican power.

Spain

The terrorist movement ETA continues to fight for independence for the Basque region. Increased local autonomy and other reforms have reduced its support, but the organisation has not faded away completely.

Morocco

The Moroccan army has been fighting the Polisario guerrillas in the Western Sahara since 1976. By building fortified lines along the borders, the Moroccans are cutting the guerrillas off from their supply bases in Algeria and Mauretania.

Namibia

The conflict between the SWAPO guerrillas and the South African controlled local forces is now over. South Africa has withdrawn, but SWAPO failed to win enough votes to overturn the new constitution in its favour. Hopefully this long-running war is now over.

South Africa

Nelson Mandela's refusal to announce the end of the ANC's 'armed struggle' offers the grim prospect of renewed terrorist violence in South Africa. Meanwhile, the fighting in Natal between the Zulus and UDF movement continues to claim lives.

Uganda

Tribal violence and government repression continue to take a steady toll of lives. The government now hosts an ANC camp housing blacks imprisoned by Nelson Mandela's 'freedom fighters'. Camps in Angola are threatened by UNITA guerrillas.

Sudan

Civil war between the Christian and Animist south and the once-again militantly Islamic north has catapulted this tragic country back to the last century. Without massive foreign aid, the government lacks the strength to overwhelm the various guerrilla armies.

Chad

French military intervention helped seal the defeat of Libyan troops, sent into Chad to support one of the many factions jockeying for power over the last 20 years. President Mitterand has thus won the latest round of 'keep your man in the capital'.

Israel

Arab resistance in the occupied territories of Gaza and the West Bank of the Jordan is only checked by constant military action. With the PLO again threatening to renew its 'armed struggle', the prospect of an urban terrorist campaign is very real.

Iraq

The ending of the Gulf War has freed Iraqi forces to deal with internal dissent, especially the Kurds. Divided between Turkey, Iran and Iraq, the Kurds have fought all three in their struggle for independence. But Iraqi army offensives, involving the use of poison gas against towns and villages, have been murderously effective.

Ethiopia

Since *glasnost* in the USSR, the Marxist rebels now identify Albania as the only upholder of the true socialist tradition. The equally Marxist government is fighting guerrillas in Eritrea and Tigre provinces and currently facing an offensive possibly aimed at the capital. Meanwhile, the population starves to death.

Laos

The country that became the most heavily bombed target of the Vietnam war is still host to Vietnamese troops. It supports the communist regime against resistance in the countryside, but the strength of opposition is difficult to determine.

Indonesia

In 1975 Indonesian troops invaded the former Portuguese colony of East Timor. The population has been resisting ever since and an estimated 230,000 people have died. The guerrilla forces do not receive much outside aid and rely mainly on captured guns and ammunition.

Battle for GOOSE GREEN

Members of 2 Para tell how they defeated three times their number in the first major land battle on the Falklands.

Weighed down by large packs, troops file ashore at San Carlos. The battle for Goose Green took place mainly because of insistence for 'some action' from London. The size of the Argentine force was not accurately known until after the battle.

"All the fire was coming my way. I fired back and emptied the magazine straight away, 20 rounds rapid towards the enemy position to keep his head down while I got into the best position I could. Whatever cover there was I found it, and there wasn't much. I changed magazines, which was difficult because I was lying down and the magazines had jammed in the pouch, so I was flapping quite a bit."

The first land battle of the Falklands campaign was at its height. Sergeant Major Norman was accompanying Lieutenant-Colonel 'H' Jones on his desperate bid to break through the Argentine defences. Their target: the settlements of Darwin and Goose Green, where a reinforced Argentine regiment was deployed in defence of the airstrip. Major Chris Keeble was second-in-command of the 2nd Battalion, the Parachute Regiment:

"The battlefield at Goose Green was a corridor about five miles long and one mile wide, flat – bare-arsed. There was no cover, and that was the most serious deficiency about it. Halfway down, running across the direction from which we would approach, was a ridgeline where they built a defensive position."

Major Keeble knew the attack had to go in under cover of darkness. "'H' wanted to try and capture the settlements of Darwin and Goose Green at night because

the battlefield was so bare. He constructed a plan to manoeuvre his three companies of about 80 men each down this corridor, supporting each other with artillery and naval gunfire from HMS *Arrow* offshore."

"That was the plan. But plans don't always work like that because on your side you have 400 people trying to make it work and, in this case, we had 1,500 people on the other side trying to screw it up."

It was cold, with a strong wind gusting to 50 knots, and it started to rain. The leading companies were soon amongst the Argentine positions. Major Neame commanded D Company:

"We advanced up the hill. They must have seen us and we attracted sporadic small-arms fire, but it was wild and ineffective. We got to their position and started to clear through it. The sections broke down to four-man fire teams and started to clear through with bullets and grenades.

Getting a grip

Attacking down the eastern side of the isthmus, A Company's early progress was halted by Argentine trenches outside Darwin. Sergeant Major Barry Norman, in charge of Lieutenant Colonel Jones' protection party, witnessed 'H's' reaction:

"The CO got on the radio and told them to get a grip, speed up and continue the movement, which they couldn't. So he said,

'I'm not having any of this,' and decided to go up and join A Company.

"I and another sergeant-major threw smoke bombs to give protection and we went through the smoke. It was good to know they couldn't see you. We got up to A Company – there were dead and injured lying around. The CO went up to the officer commanding and asked him what the situation was and why they were bogged down; what were they going to do about it? When the decision was made, everybody got in a straight line and we called for mortar fire with smoke and went over the top again and started for the Argentine positions.

"As we got halfway the smoke ran out. It was windy and the smoke didn't stay long; it was as if we were on a snooker table, flat and no protection at all. We sustained quite a few casualties, some of them fatal, in that initial burst from the Argentine positions.

"There was more fire and the smoke cleared – the adjutant and the second-in-command of A Company were killed. So we went to ground and again there was nowhere else to go. We could have reversed and got shot in the back. We couldn't go forward because it was too far to go.

"The CO said, 'Right, follow me.' He got up and ran off to the right, off the feature, so we had exposed ourselves to the enemy. We were running diagonally across his front, and down to the right.

Right: British troops were well wrapped up against the bleak weather conditions. Many of the Argentine conscripts came from the warm north of the country and were not prepared to spend weeks on end living in the open on the Falklands.

British Paratrooper Falklands war, 1982

The paratroopers who took part in the battle for Goose Green were amongst the toughest professional soldiers in the world. But not all their kit was of the same high quality.

Smock
Paratroops were issued with Arctic windproof smocks in place of their paratroop smocks. These have a wired hood, large pockets, and buttons that can be opened while wearing gloves.

Overtrousers
SAS windproof overtrousers were worn on top of a quilted 'Chinese fighting suit' and Army issue Arctic long johns.

Backpack
The paras used the standard SAS/Para Bergen, in which they kept everything from rations to mortar bombs, spare clothes, mess tins, sleeping bags, spare water and first-aid tins.

Boots
2 Para were issued with Royal Marine Ski-March boots on the way south, but they never had time to break them in. They wore their normal Boots DMS (shown here) or Boots Combat High, neither of which were able to cope with the wet conditions on the Falklands.

7.62 mm Assault Rifle
Known as the SLR (Self-Loading Rifle) in the British Army, this is another version of the powerful and reliable FN FAL also used by the Argentines. Normally issued with eight 20-round magazines, some British troops were carrying up to 14 when they went into action.

2 Para's approach to the Goose Green position was reported on BBC World Service before the attack went in. Although the Argentines did not seem to benefit from this incredible error, it did not do much for army/media relations.

"We went round into a re-entrant between two Argentine positions, one we had cleared and one we had tried to clear. Suddenly someone shouted, 'Watch out, there's a trench to the left!' Hearing that, instinct took over and instead of running I dived and hit the ground as fast as I could, just as they opened fire on us. The CO had got beyond the next trench and was obscured from the enemy because of the way the land was going.

'H' is shot

"I looked out of the corner of my eye and saw the CO take his sub-machine gun and start charging up the hill towards the trench I was firing at. But he was coming into view of the Argentine trenches behind us. He kept on going. I shouted at him to watch his back because I could see what was going to happen.

"He got to within six or seven feet of that trench and was shot from the trenches behind. You could see the rounds striking the ground behind him, coming gradually towards him, and they shot him in the back. The impact of the rounds hitting him pushed him right over the top of the trench he was going for."

With the death of Lieutenant Colonel Jones, command of the battle passed to Major Chris Keeble. He inherited a desperate situation: A Company pinned down on one side of the isthmus and B Company blocked the other side by a machine-gun nest in the rubble of an old building called Boca House.

"All that ran through my mind, and eventually I got a clear picture. It was as clear a picture as I was ever going to get. I then set off towards Johnny Crosland's B Company. We took with us the MILAN anti-tank missiles . . .

"As we set off over the hill, in came two Pucará aircraft and strafed the position behind us, but we had to ignore them. In the time it took me to get up to B Company, Phil Neame – the canny Phil Neame who commanded D Company – had realised that he could outflank the Boca House position by slipping his company down on to the beach. There was a small wall between the edge of the grassland and the beach. His men crawled 800 or 900 metres along this little shelf until they were adjacent to the enemy defensive position . . . brilliant.

"With a combination of MILAN anti-tank missiles which fire over 2,000 metres and have pinpoint accuracy, we were able to destroy the enemy machine-guns which were pinning us down."

Meanwhile the trench from which 'H' Jones had been shot had been blown apart by a direct hit from a 66-mm light anti-tank rocket. The destruction of this trench fatally undermined the whole Argentine line because, instead of staggering their positions to give mutually supporting fire, they had dug them in a single line.

D Company reached the schoolhouse at Goose Green and took it out with 66-mm LAWs and white phosphorus grenades. As the attack on the schoolhouse went in, Argentine resistance appeared to collapse and white flags were seen waving near the airfield. D Company's 12 platoon commander, Lieutenant Barry, stood up and walked towards two Argentinians who had their hands in the air. Sergeant John Meredith was concerned:

"I saw him talking to two Argentinians who seemed to be worried about the firing still going on at the schoolhouse. Then, for some reason, Mr Barry put a rifle against a fence. Suddenly, a burst of fire, probably from someone who wasn't aware that a surrender was taking place, came whistling over the top. The Argentines who'd been sitting there reacted immediately by picking up their weapons and firing.

Three more deaths

"Mr Barry was killed instantly. Knight, the radio operator, killed two with his SMG but Corporal Smith, who was trying to give covering fire with a 66, and CPC Sullivan were also killed. Shevill was wounded in the shoulder and the hip. There was now an awful lot of firing going on.

"I got across another section and picked up a machine-gun and knocked off three Argies with a couple of bursts each. Then, as I moved again, I took out two more. We moved forward and took their position and dealt with Shevill, who was badly hurt."

After 15 hours' fighting, the Argentines were boxed in around the settlement, confused, and painfully aware that no help was forthcoming from the main Argentine forces 35 miles away at Port Stanley. But with last light approaching, Major Keeble was anxious to avoid an all-out assault. 2 Para were exhausted and the Argentines had locked up 114 British civilians in the centre of Goose Green.

"I sent two Argentine officers down into the settlement with a note which explained my two options: surrender or take the military consequences. They took the surrender option and we met in a small hut on the airfield. I met the three military commanders there and they agreed to my terms. They would assemble on the sports field.

"Eventually about 150 people in three ranks marched up and formed a hollow square. An officer in an Argentine air force uniform walked up to me and saluted. I asked for his pistol and took it. When we looked closely we saw that these people weren't soldiers at all. They were airmen.

"I said, 'Where are the soldiers?'

"He indicated the settlement and said, 'They are coming.'

"Three or four of us moved forward – there were only about eight of us altogether at the surrender – to look down into the settlement. There, to our amazement, must have been 1,000 men, marching up in three ranks. We just held our breath.

"Somebody murmured, 'I hope they don't change their minds.'"

Goose Green was an incredible victory and an outstanding performance by 2 Para. Lieutenant Colonel Jones won a posthumous Victoria Cross.

Goose Green: May 1982

The lack of cover made it essential for the British attack to go in under cover of darkness. But night battles are difficult to control, and as dawn approached the battle was still raging. The action finally ended after 15 hours, when the disorganised Argentine forces were persuaded to surrender.

An after-the-battle souvenir snapshot of a wrecked Argentine Pucará ground attack aircraft. Two were shot down by 2 Para.

The landings at San Carlos took the Argentines on the Falklands by surprise: they were expecting an attack on their main concentration of forces around Port Stanley. Even as the Marines and Paras began to march across the island, the first major battle of the campaign was taking place south of the landings, at the tiny settlements of Darwin and Goose Green.

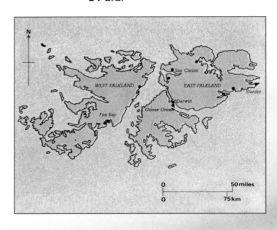

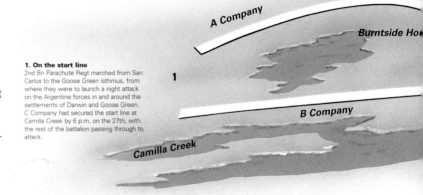

1. On the start line
2nd Bn Parachute Regt marched from San Carlos to the Goose Green isthmus, from where they were to launch a night attack on the Argentine forces in and around the settlements of Darwin and Goose Green. C Company had secured the start line at Camilla Creek by 6 p.m. on the 27th, with the rest of the battalion passing through to attack.

"I sat down and I thought: I'm lucky. I went numb, and the whole implication of what had happened throughout the day, the people who had died and the casualties I had seen started appearing before me. There was an eerie silence; it was pitch dark. Freezing. The mind just ran riot and I felt tears trickling down the side of my face when I thought about good blokes who had died that day and the fact that more were likely to die tomorrow."

Sergeant Major Barry Norman, 'H' Jones' bodyguard, speaking after the first day

Above: The sense of victory came when the red, white and blue of the Union Jack was run up in place of the blue and white Argentine flag.

The sad aftermath ot any battle is exemplified in the bodies of the young men who did not survive. The 22 British fatalities in the battle included two pilots, while the Argentines lost some 60 men, mostly conscripts.

Goose Green after the battle. Members of 2 Para's Patrol Company pose with some 'liberated' Argentine air force rations outside a sheep shearing shed.

6. Victory
By midnight, D Company had taken the Airstrip, B Company had cut the Argentines off, and the rest of the battalion was pressing exhaustedly in on Goose Green. At 1 a.m. the Argentine commander made contact with the British, and at 8.30 two captured Argentines were sent in with an ultimatum. The Argentines surrendered at noon.

Goose Green

Schoolhouse

Airfield

2. First attack
A Company attacked Burntside House just after 2.30 a.m., only to find that the Argentines positioned there had gone. B Company, followed by D Company, continued down the other side of the isthmus, bypassing isolated Argentine posts in the dark and the driving rain.

Darwin

Coronation Point

Argentine Defence Line

5. Closing in
The attack on Goose Green itself began at 3 p.m. The Schoolhouse was attacked by part of D Company, and saw the death of Lieutenant Berry's party, shot down after the forces in the building had surrendered. It was probably a genuine mistake, but it enraged the tough British paratroopers.

Darwin Hill

3. Colonel 'H' Jones killed
A Company reached the main Argentine defensive line at Darwin Hill without difficulty, but was then pinned down by fierce fire. Colonel 'H' Jones, the battalion commander, was killed while attempting to lead the attack personally.

A Company's advance

Boca House

4. Argentines outflanked
B Company had been halted at the ruins of Boca House by a well-placed machine-gun nest. The coming of daylight meant artillery fire and air attacks could be expected. However, the position was outflanked by D Company, which crawled along the beach, and a breakthrough by A Company on the other side of the isthmus forced the defenders to withdraw.

B and D Company's advance

ADVANCE TO CONTACT
2 Para made its way down the mile-wide stretch of land, taking or bypassing isolated Argentine positions in the dark. The advance was brought up short by strong Argentine defences along the low ridge near Darwin.

FIRE AND MANOEUVRE

Firing a rifle in combat is very different from target shooting on the range. You still have to place your shots carefully, but you must stop the enemy from firing back effectively. This is achieved by fire and manoeuvre: keeping some men firing while others advance toward the enemy position.

The infantry soldier's job is to get to close quarters and destroy the enemy. He does this by fire and manoeuvre: this skill is as basic to his survival on the battlefield as breathing in and out. In order to get close enough to kill the enemy, you have to advance on his position. But while you move, the enemy is free to fire at you; so someone must keep firing to make them keep their heads down. This is called 'keeping one foot on the ground at all times'. At the lowest level it works with one soldier firing while the other in the two-man team moves forward. The same principle is used when a whole company is attacking: one platoon moves, supported by the other platoons.

General instructions:

1 The basic unit for fire and manoeuvre is the fireteam: four men who fight as two pairs.

2 One team moves while the other fires at the enemy position. Well-aimed shots will force the enemy to keep his head down.

3 When the fireteam gets very close to the enemy, it no longer moves by pairs. Each pair of soldiers advances by fire and manoeuvre, one shooting while the other moves.

4 Soldiers must be careful not to cross their partner's arc of fire. They could be shot by their own side or stop their partner firing, which would leave the enemy free to shoot.

5 Soldiers must be aware of where their rifle is pointing at all times. Running about with safety off and finger near the trigger is a recipe for accidents. Make sure the muzzle never points at a partner.

6 Accidents are also avoided by keeping the finger off the trigger and rested on the trigger guard when moving.

7 It may be obvious, but it is essential for soldiers to keep the muzzle clear of their own body, especially their feet.

8 Anyone who drops his rifle must check that the muzzle is not blocked with earth, as this could cause a breech explosion on firing.

9 Rifles are always carried loaded and made ready, but with the safety catch on. To ensure reliable performance, rifles should be cleaned and oiled at least once a day.

10 Sights should be set at 300 m at all times. Some rifles have folding battle sights, which should be folded up ready to fire.

11 Automatic fire should be reserved for close-quarter battle, and shot from the hip. Automatic from the shoulder is a waste of ammo – if there is time to take aim, there is time to fire an aimed shot.

Breaking cover

1 Never move until you know your partner is down in a good fire position and is firing.

2 Crawl backwards and to the side of the cover you were in, so that you do not pop up in the place you have fired from.

3 Note the position of your partner, the direction the enemy fire is coming from, and the next available piece of cover.

4 Burst forward into the standing position and zigzag forward into the area of cover. Do not stand upright. Keep low with your weapon well forward, ready to fire at any target that appears at close range.

5 Dive towards the cover and then crawl into it.

Providing covering fire

1 Look through or round cover rather than over it.

2 Get into a good fire position with your sights on the source of enemy fire and begin to put pressure on the trigger.

3 Fire a few aimed shots at the enemy position, which is the signal for your partner to move.

4 With a SUSAT sight, watch out for your partner, who could stray into your arc. Look up every few shots so that you can see what is going on.

5 The closer you get to the enemy, the more rounds you need to fire to stop them shooting back. You may need to switch to short, aimed bursts.

6 Never tell your partner to move until you are actually putting aimed shots down on the enemy position.

Advance to contact

1 Advance to contact with the weapon in your shoulder, covering your arc over your sights. This enables you to return fire immediately.

2 Look for the next piece of cover you are going to use if you are shot at. Look into the areas where the enemy are likely to be.

3 Keep off open areas and choose lines of advance that offer cover from fire and view.

4 Make sure you are well spaced out and that both you and your partner can fire to the front.

5 Split the ground up ahead of you into tactical bounds. At the end of each bound, stop and examine the next few hundred metres of the route from cover before moving on.

Reacting to enemy fire

1 Dash towards the nearest cover. If the enemy is very close, fire a short burst to put him off his aim.

2 Get down fast and crawl into cover.

3 Look through or round cover to try to find the enemy.

4 Fire aimed shots at the enemy position to stop him firing at you. After a few shots you should change position by crawling or rolling to the side.

5 Indicate the target to your partner.

6 If you get a target, fire single aimed shots at the centre of the body mass presented to you.

Fire positions

1 If you are right-handed, always shoot round to the right so that your body is not exposed.

2 Pick cover that will stop incoming high-velocity rounds. Small trees and shrubs or even a single brick wall are not enough.

3 Always check your muzzle clearance when shooting through cover.

4 Never fire leaning out of building windows: fire from the shadows of the room.

5 Do not use obvious cover: a fold in the ground is better than an isolated tree or wall.

6 Fire from the first floor rather than the ground floor; then you can move back into the building to avoid return fire from enemy at ground level.

Moving in contact

1 As you get closer to the enemy he has a better chance of hitting you, so you must move in shorter dashes. At 300 m you can run standing up about 5 m. At 200 this is reduced to three to five paces; and at under 100 m you will have to use short dashes from cover to cover or crawl in the dead ground.

2 Watch out for the unexpected enemy trench. Don't concentrate so hard on the trench you have been ordered to attack that you blunder into an unnoticed position.

3 Use smoke to cover movement in open ground.

4 Use covered approaches as far as possible. Pick the route that gives cover from fire and view.

5 At close range you cannot afford to change mags. Put a fresh mag on when you get to the last piece of cover before the enemy trench, and fit your bayonet.

Engaging target at various ranges

1 Your rifle is usually zeroed to strike the centre of the target at 300 m.

2 Aim low when shooting at a small target at close range, e.g. the head of a soldier in a trench. It is always better to hit low rather than miss high.

3 Watch your strike. At long range you will have to estimate the range to the target and aim off for wind. At 500 m you are unlikely to get a first-round hit. Aim low; watch the strike of the round and correct accordingly. If your rounds are going high you will not see where they strike the ground.

4 You will learn to judge distance in training, but comparing how much of a man is covered by the foresight of the rifle at different ranges is a good technique.

5 Having shot at a target that seems to fall immediately, fire at the place where the target disappeared from view and then move on to fire at all the likely places he would go for cover.

6 Aimed single shots on rapid fire are almost always better than full auto!

Stoppages and changing mags

1 Always count your rounds so that you have an idea when to change mags. One way is to put a tracer round third from the bottom of the mag.

2 Shout 'Magazine change' to your partner so that he knows he has to start shooting.

3 Drop the empty magazine inside your smock rather than in your webbing. Thus there is no chance of your reloading with an empty.

4 Reload with a fresh mag as fast as possible. Cock the weapon, and don't worry if there was already a round in the chamber. This saves time, which could save your life.

5 The best way to tell your partner you are back in business is to fire a few rounds rapidly into the target.

6 If you are unlucky enough to get a stoppage, shout: "Stoppage!" and your partner will put down covering fire.

Close quarter battle

1 In close country where the enemy is likely to be engaged at short range, keep the weapon in your shoulder with the safety catch off.

2 The trigger finger is kept outside the trigger guard on uneven ground, but rests lightly on the trigger when checking areas that could conceal enemy.

3 Keep both eyes open and scan your arc with the muzzle, roughly following where you are looking. Both you and your partner will have an interlocking arc of observation.

4 If you see something suspicious, fire a few shots rapid or a short burst. Then get into cover and fire aimed shots at the enemy.

5 Give a target indication to your partner and fire and manoeuvre towards the target.

6 At very close range, under 10 m, you can use the underarm assault technique to engage the target.

THE GENERAL PURPOSE MACHINE GUN

Machine-guns have dominated infantry fighting since World War I. For the last 50 years, the most important type has been the General Purpose Machine Gun (GPMG). Firing the same 7.62-mm bullet as contemporary rifles, GPMGs have provided the bulk of infantry units' firepower in battles from Vietnam to the Gulf War.

The grass-covered slopes were already in the iron grip of a heavy Falklands frost. It crackled underfoot as the Royal Marines moved cautiously through the night. Ahead, the ridgelines of Mount Harriet could dimly be made out, and the sinister shape of a bunker loomed out of the darkness. The leading troops halted, but too late. A parachute flare burst overhead and drifted in the cold wind, its eerie light betraying them to the defenders. Tracer rounds stabbed out from the bunkers as Argentine machine-guns opened fire.

There were six machine-gun posts on Mount Harriet: the backbone of the defence.

Supported by some sniper teams, they held up the Royal Marines for nearly five hours. They were silenced only by a deadly combination of MILAN anti-tank missiles and well-coordinated infantry attacks.

Machine-guns played an equally important role in the British forces. The moment Mount Harriet was secured, 42 Commando brought forward 10,000 rounds of ammunition for its General Purpose Machine Guns (GPMGs). The final objective, a rocky outcrop 500 metres further on, was lashed by the concentrated fire of 15 GPMGs before L Company assaulted it.

The term 'General Purpose Machine Gun' (GPMG) is used to describe a weapon that serves two main purposes: the **light** and the

A British GPMG roars into action, proving that Sylvester Stallone is not the only man to fire a machine-gun from the hip. But in reality this technique is only to be used if the enemy get to within a few feet.

In 1917 German machine-gunners were given oxygen tanks to survive British gas attacks

Sustained Fire (SF) roles. In the light role, the gun is deployed as part of a rifle-armed infantry section. One soldier fires the weapon from a bipod and another assists him, carrying ammunition and helping to feed the belts into the gun. The machine-gun is as mobile as the rest of the section, providing vital firepower in both attack and defence. Sustained Fire means exactly that: shooting five or 10-round bursts for prolonged periods, perhaps for several hours. By mounting the gun on a firmly positioned tripod and changing the barrel regularly, a machine-gun can be fired with astonishing accuracy over ranges of up to 3000 metres.

Machine-gun ammunition

All the leading GPMGs fire 7.62-mm bullets. The NATO machine-guns fire the same ammunition as their rifles of the same calibre: the British SLR or West German G3. The excellent Russian PK GPMG also fires a 7.62-mm cartridge, but it is a slightly more powerful rifle round dating back to the 1890s.

Both are very dangerous. Concentrated bursts of GPMG fire will penetrate single brick walls, chew through breeze blocks and shatter the roofs of houses. Only the most

Machine-guns on the Western Front

The World War I battles on the Western Front were dominated by machine-guns. Superbly engineered weapons like the Vickers gun or the German Maxim were capable of firing for hour after hour. Well-trained crews could change a barrel in the twinkling of an eye. So long as the water and ammunition supply lasted, these machine-guns could hold off large numbers of attacking infantry, inflicting horrific casualties.

The British Army formed a specialist Machine Gun Corps in 1915. This developed the Vickers to its full potential, firing to over 3,000 yards, and using indirect fire. These tactics were reapplied in World War II and were coming back into fashion even as withdrawal of the GPMG from British infantry sections took hold in 1990.

British machine-gunners fire a Vickers gun during the battle of the Somme. The sights are set for 2,200 yards, but the gun could fire at up to 3,000: twice the effective range of most modern GPMGs.

The Vickers gun was the best of the World War I heavy machine-guns: the British Army did not replace it until 1968. Its capacity for sustained fire has gone down in legend. During the Great War, some Vickers guns were fired for 12 hours or more without stopping for more than a quick barrel change.

GENERAL PURPOSE MACHINE-GUN Reference File

43

USA

M60 general-purpose machine-gun

World War II highlighted the shortcomings of the elderly machine-gun designs in service with the US Army. The Americans were so impressed by the German MG42 that they attempted to copy it, but errors in converting metric to Imperial measurements made their version unworkable. After the war the US Army adopted a new design, chambered for the 7.62-mm cartridge, but heavily influenced by the World War II German machine-gun.

The M60 was used throughout the Vietnam War and machine-gun sections provided the bulk of US infantry firepower in countless jungle battles.

Its ability to rip through the vegetation and enemy cover was highly satisfying, and its stopping power unquestioned. When North Vietnamese forces attempted to overrun American positions in desperate night attacks, the fire from M60 positions was often the deciding factor. The NVA knew this, and M60 gun teams were often singled out for destruction.

In Vietnam the M60 earned the nickname 'The Pig', partly from affection but also from irritation. Although a powerful weapon, the M60 had several poor design features and was never as reliable as the Belgian FN MAG or Soviet PK. Major alterations

The M60 was the Americans' main machine-gun in Vietnam.

have led to the M60E3, recently adopted by the US Marine Corps.

Specification
Cartridge: 7.62-mm × 51 NATO
Weight: 10.5 kg
Length: 1105 mm
Cyclic rate of fire: 550 rounds per minute
Practical rate of fire: 200 rpm
Users: United States Army, Marine Corps and Air Force plus Australia and most Asian nations supplied by the USA. Small numbers have been acquired by the Provisional IRA.

solid cover will protect a soldier from GPMG fire. At close range, even light armoured vehicles such as the British Scorpion or Russian BRDM can be penetrated by 7.62-mm machine-guns.

The first successful GPMGs were fielded by the Germans during World War II. Until then, all armies used one type of machine-gun designed for sustained fire and another to operate in the light role with the infantry sections.

Sustained-fire machine-guns dominated the battlefields of World War I. Their killing power was demonstrated most conspicuously on 1 July 1916. On the first day of its offensive on the Somme, the British Army suffered 57,000 casualties: most of them from German Maxim machine-guns. Yet these deadly weapons were very cumbersome and demanded a large crew to supply them with cooling water, ammunition and spare barrels.

*Above: An **SAS** patrol in North Africa returns from behind enemy lines in trucks bristling with machine-guns. Most are Vickers 'K' guns. The drum magazine contained 100 .303 bullets.*

Left: An MG34 in service with the first German troops deployed to North Africa. In the desert it was important to use gun oil very sparingly since it attracted sand.

The Professional's View:

General-purpose machine-guns

"The M60 machine-gun was a superior weapon. It could be fired from a tripod, which was too heavy and which no Marine Corps gunner ever carried into the bush, or the bipod, two attached legs that swung from under the barrel, or it could be fired from the hip. The recoil from firing would actually help hold the weight of the barrel up and the gun on target. I could put out 550 rounds per minute with a maximum range of 3750 metres. I was sold on the gun."

PFC John M. Clark, 5th US Marine Regiment, Vietnam, 1968

44

BELGIUM

FN MAG General Purpose Machine Gun

The FN MAG is the most successful general-purpose machine-gun produced since the war. The British Army is one of 75 nations to have bought it and, despite many NATO armies reverting to light machine-guns during the 1980s, it is destined to serve well into the 21st century. A highly reliable, gas-operated weapon, the FN MAG has a regulator to allow the gunner to increase the gas supply to overcome resistance in adverse conditions. This can be used to control the exact rate of fire – from 600 to 1000 rounds per minute. At its lowest rate, the FN MAG will produce single aimed shots for one squeeze of the trigger, making it a surprisingly accurate weapon in the hands of an experienced gunner. Barrel changes on the FN MAG are very simple, and it works very well in the sustained fire role. New ammunition is being developed to increase its maximum range to over 2,000 metres.

The FN MAG has seen action in Angola, Namibia, the Rhodesian war, Mozambique and many other wars. It has frequently been used by both sides – perhaps most notably in the Falklands war, where it was the standard GPMG of both the British and Argentine armies.

The FN MAG, known to the British Army as the GPMG, was used by both sides in the Falklands war.

Specification
Cartridge: 7.62 mm × 51 NATO
Weight: 10.9 kg
Length: 1232 mm
Cyclic rate of fire: 750-1000 rounds per minute
Practical rate of fire: 250 rounds per minute
Users: Too numerous to list in detail, they include the British Army which designates it as the L7A2 GPMG; it is manufactured under licence in South America and Asia.

7.62-mm machine-gun penetration

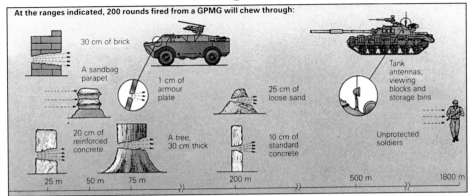

At the ranges indicated, 200 rounds fired from a GPMG will chew through:

30 cm of brick

A sandbag parapet

1 cm of armour plate

25 cm of loose sand

Tank antennas, viewing blocks and storage bins

20 cm of reinforced concrete

A tree, 30 cm thick

10 cm of standard concrete

Unprotected soldiers

25 m   50 m   75 m   200 m   500 m   1800 m

Typical GPMGs fire 7.62-mm bullets that are travelling at over 800 metres per second when they leave the barrel. As they travel further away from the gun, their speed decreases and so does their ability to penetrate cover. But a 7.62-mm round will still have more than enough power left to kill an unprotected person at its maximum effective range of 1800 metres.

A graphic demonstration of GPMG power: a target placed behind a brick wall has been perforated by a hail of 7.62-mm bullets.

Plumes of steam made them hard to conceal, and when the water supply ran out, crews were sometimes reduced to using their urine instead.

The size and weight of the big water-cooled machine-guns restricted them to defensive operations, so most armies introduced lighter weapons that could keep up with the infantry during an attack. The British infantry adopted the Lewis light machine-gun, which it soon relied on more than its rifles.

When Hitler began the German re-armament programme, the German forces adopted many new weapons. One of them was the MG34: a belt-fed machine-gun designed to perform both roles. It obviously made sense to standardise on one machine-gun. Soldiers would only have to learn to operate one system, and the supply of spares would be simplified. But it was no easy matter to design a multi-purpose machine-gun. To be capable of sustained fire, the weapon needs to be cooled to prevent overheating. To survive the punishing recoil forces of prolonged automatic fire it must be very strongly built.

45

BELGIUM

AA52 (Arme Automatique Transformable Model 52)

The French army is still equipped with this mediocre GPMG, introduced as part of a programme of new infantry weapons immediately after World War II. Most AA52s in service today are chambered for the 7.62-mm NATO cartridge, but the original weapon fired the French 7.5-mm rifle round that is still encountered among reserve forces and in French influenced areas of Africa. The AA52 is not gas-operated: it operates by delayed blowback using a two-piece bolt unit and special arrangements to cope with case extraction. This sort of mechanism is unusual on weapons firing full power rifle ammunition because the recoil is so severe. Like most blowback operated weapons, the AA52 flings its empty cases violently away from the gun. The cases are distinctly marked and are often split in the process. At the time of its introduction, this case-chewing was claimed to be an advantage since it stopped Viet Minh or Algerian guerrillas re-loading them.

The AA52 is one of a series of French infantry weapons which have never attracted serious foreign interest because of their odd ammunition and idiosyncratic design. Barrel changes are awkward when the gun is fired from its bipod. The gun must be cocked when a loaded belt is carried.

Specification
Cartridge: 7.5-mm M1929 or 7.62-mm NATO
Weight: 9.8kg
Length: 1140mm
Cyclic rate of fire: 650-700 rounds per minute
Practical rate of fire: 200 rpm

The AA52 is one of a succession of mediocre weapons produced by the French since World War II.

Users: French army and the forces of African nations still effectively controlled by France

---

46

Former USSR

PK (Pulemyot Kalashnikova)

The PK is the Russian equivalent of the popular FN MAG. Used by all former Warsaw Pact forces, it has won a reputation as one of the finest GPMGs in service since the war. It fires the old Soviet 7.62-mm rifle round developed at the end of the last century; with its pronounced rim, it is not the easiest cartridge to use in a machine-gun. However, the Russians have developed a modified version of the Kalashnikov action to manage the ammunition. Its only major problem is the use of a non-disintegrating belt, which can get in the gunner's way if he has to move.

Using this elderly cartridge gave the Soviet infantry two types of 7.62-mm ammunition that were not interchangeable. But the PK is as thoroughly reliable as the Kalashnikov rifles, and its powerful round will penetrate 28cm of earth, 17.8cm of sand and even 12.7cm of concrete. Fired from a bipod in the light role, it uses 50-round belts. When mounted on a tripod for sustained fire, 250-round boxes are employed. With a simple barrel change facility, light recoil and impressive accuracy, the PK has performed well in Vietnam, the Middle East and Africa. Like the NATO armies, the Russians are abandoning their 7.62-mm machine-guns in the light role. The PK is mostly replaced by a heavy-barreled version of the AK-47, the Russian equivalent of the British LSW.

Specification
Cartridge: 7.62-mm × 54R
Weight: 9kg
Length: 1160mm
Cyclic rate of fire: 650 rounds per minute
Practical rate of fire: 250 rpm
Users: USSR and all allies and satellite

The PK is another superb Russian weapon: powerful, reliable, and straightforward in its operation. It was used throughout the Warsaw Pact.

nations; widely used in Africa and Asia by regular and guerrilla forces

British, French and Russian forces had little incentive to rise to this design challenge. They had vast stocks of SF machine-guns and LMGs that were considered perfectly adequate. But the Germans were effectively starting from scratch. Their revolutionary GPMG was adequate in either role. It was not as good an SF gun as the Vickers; and it lacked the accuracy of the Bren gun. But it could manage both roles to an acceptable standard.

German technology

The MG34 was followed by the MG42, which narrowed the gap in both fields. A two-man team could manage it in the light role, and there was no doubting its efficiency at sustained fire. All Allied soldiers came to recognise its distinctive sound, but it was especially effective on the Eastern Front, scything down wave after wave of Russian infantry. Its design formed the basis of most GPMGs developed after the war, including the American M60 and the Belgian FN MAG.

The FN MAG has proved highly successful

Left: An M60 spits empty brass cases into the sand. The bipod is permanently fitted to the barrel, which makes a quick barrel change rather difficult.

47

GERMANY

MG3 general-purpose machine-gun

The current German Army GPMG is a slightly modified version of the wartime German MG42. This appeared in 1942 and set the standard by which subsequent GPMGs have been judged. Designed for simplicity of production, its revolutionary locking system proved highly reliable even in adverse conditions. All opponents of the German army learned to recognise the MG42's distinctive sound – like a sheet of canvas tearing, or a child running a stick very quickly along a fence. Its cyclic rate of fire was 1,200 rounds per minute: 20 bullets a second!

Approximately one million MG42s were manufactured by 1945. When the West German army came into being,

this superb machine-gun was re-adopted. Altered to take the 7.62-mm NATO cartridge instead of the wartime 7.92-mm round, the gun was redesignated MG1. There were a few minor changes to the bolt and feed mechanism, but it was essentially the same weapon. Some MG42s were not altered at all, apart from the change of ammunition, and these became known as MG2s. The current MG3 is the result of further modification: it can use disintegrating link belts and the ejection port is bigger.

Specification
Cartridge: 7.62-mm NATO
Weight: 11.6 kg

Length: 1225 mm
Cyclic rate of fire: 1,200-1,300 rounds per minute. Italian-made version is 700-900 rpm using a heavier bolt
Practical rate of fire: 250 rounds per minute
Users: Germany, Denmark, Norway, Portugal and Italy

The MG3 is a slightly modified version of the World War II German MG42 machine-gun. It retains the original gun's very high rate of fire.

48

GERMANY

Heckler & Koch HK21

There have been many attempts to build families of rifles and machine-guns based on a common design, using as many of the same parts as possible. This simplifies training, makes the supply of spares easier and reduces manufacturing costs. But few such systems have actually entered widespread service. The Kalashnikov rifles and light machine-guns are the exception. The German company Heckler & Koch produced a succession of machine-gun versions of its G3 7.62-mm rifle; the HK21 and 21A1 are the latest variants of this family. All are based on the rifle's operation, but take either box magazines or belt feed.

The HK21 shares 48 per cent of its

parts with the G3 rifle – a very useful feature for an army using the G3 already. It is much lighter than GPMGs in service, and is slightly shorter. But despite a barrel change facility and versions chambered for 5.56-mm or even Soviet 7.62-mm × 39, it has not proved popular. Most major armies ended the 20th century with general purpose machine guns adopted in the 1950s or 1960s. Such was the success of these weapons that there is little impetus for new designs.

Specification
Cartridge: 7.62-mm NATO
Weight: 7.3 kg
Length: 1020 mm
Cyclic rate of fire: 850 rounds per minute
Practical rate of fire: 250 rpm
Users: HK21 sold to Portugal only

The HK21 is one of a large series of GPMGs produced mainly for export. Closely based on the G3 rifle, this makes training and the supply of spares much easier.

The machin
World War

Until World War II, machine guns were divided into light, bipod-mounted guns that were issued to each infantry section; and heavier machine-guns that fired from tripods. In the 1930s, the Germans introduced the idea of a General Purpose Machine Gun. The success of their MG42 made a deep impression on the Allies: NATO and Warsaw Pact forces all adopted GPMGs during the 1950s.

British infantry relied heavily on their GPMGs in the Falklands. Note how other members of the section are carrying linked belts of 7.62-mm ammunition for the gun.

and is used by more than 20 armies: it supplanted the veteran Vickers gun in the British Army in 1968. The American M60 was handicapped by having no carrying handle; this meant the gunner needed an asbestos glove to change the barrel. Since the barrel was permanently fixed to the bipod, the gun teams had to carry excess weight. A barrel change at night, under fire, was a severe test of manual dexterity. But its 7.62-mm bullets could plough through the Vietnamese jungle, even drilling through trees. For all its faults, the M60 provided the US infantry platoons with essential heavy firepower.

During the 1980s the NATO armies followed the American lead and adopted rifles chambered for a standard 5.56-mm cartridge. But these are too light for long-range sustained fire, and the machine-guns chambered to fire them are turning back the clock to the 1930s. The British Army's Light Support Weapon (LSW) is no more than an SA80 rifle with a heavy barrel. It only fires from a box magazine, and sustained fire is out of the question.

The idea of a machine-gun for both tasks has been killed off by the new-calibre rifle ammunition. Existing weapons will soldier on, but mainly in the SF role. Whether this will lead to a new generation of purpose-built SF machine-guns is open to question. But since weapons like the Russian PK or the Belgian FN MAG are highly effective SF weapons, they are likely to be in service for many years to come.

Weapons like this M249 Squad Automatic Weapon – the US designation for the FN Minimi – are replacing GPMGs. The M249 fires the 5.56-mm rounds now adopted by all NATO forces as their standard rifle round.

 Bren Mk 1

Above: Each 10-man section of British infantry was issued with a Bren gun. Highly accurate and reliable, this Czech weapon remains one of the best light machine-guns ever made.

MG42

The very high rate of fire of the MG42 gave it a very distinctive sound, more like the ripping of canvas than the steady stutter of a Vickers gun.

The MG42's incredible rate of fire made it vitally important for the gun team to be able to change the barrel easily. The rate of fire made the MG42 harder to control when shooting from a bipod: it was nowhere near as accurate as the Bren gun. But the sheer volume of fire made it very hard for the target to shoot back.

gun in

Vickers 303

Right: New ammunition issued before World War II pushed the Vickers gun's range to over 4,500 yards. Platoons of four Vickers guns were used for long-range indirect fire.

The distinctive banana-shaped magazine of the Bren gun was built this way to accommodate the British .303 rimmed rifle cartridge.

The Bren gun was a modified version of the Czech ZB vz 26 light machine-gun. Gas operated and simply constructed, it was a 'soldier-proof' weapon. 1150 mm long, it weighed 10.15 kg unloaded. The 30-round magazine could be emptied in four seconds, but with three or four round bursts the Bren was almost as accurate as a rifle.

The Vickers was cooled by this sleeve, which was filled with water. This would boil after 600 rounds of rapid fire, the steam passing down a tube into a condensing can. It could then be poured back into the sleeve. When gunners ran short of water, urine was the usual substitute.

The Vickers was normally fired at a rate of one 250-round belt every two minutes. Four-second bursts of 25-30 rounds were fired at 6-8 second intervals. For 'rapid fire' the interval between bursts was reduced to 3-4 seconds.

The basic Vickers course lasted two months in 1939 and it took much longer to become truly expert on the gun. The weighty manual had 11 pages of Immediate Action and stoppage drills! A six-man crew was needed to move the gun – the tripod alone weighed 22 kg.

The MG42 was developed because the first German GPMG, the MG34, could not be manufactured fast enough for wartime demands. A new locking system allowed it to produce an unheard-of 1,200 rounds per minute.

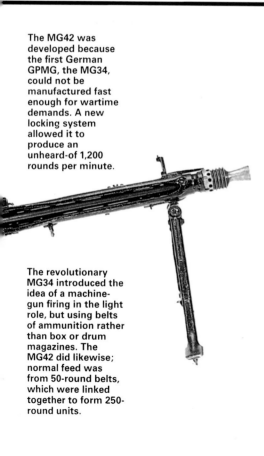

The revolutionary MG34 introduced the idea of a machine-gun firing in the light role, but using belts of ammunition rather than box or drum magazines. The MG42 did likewise; normal feed was from 50-round belts, which were linked together to form 250-round units.

MG42 Fire Support

The MG42 set up for sustained fire. By having the same weapon in both roles, the Germans simplified training and the supply of spare parts. The modern West German army uses a modified version of the MG42 today.

An experienced German gun team could change the barrel of their MG42 in about five seconds flat. A change was required after 250 rounds at rapid rate: the Sustained Fire equipment included several spares.

With its bipod the MG42 weighed 11.5 kg, not significantly heavier than the Bren gun. Fitted to a tripod, it had an effective range of about 2500 metres.

MACHINE GUNS:

HOW THEY WORK

A machine-gun is a heavy piece of kit that is made as robust as possible. It's designed to survive the mud and dirt of the battlefield, and be carried on every type of vehicle and helicopter, being shaken until it rattles. At the end of all that it has to be operated by any soldier, and spew out bullets accurately and when they're needed.

Unlike a rifle, where the bullets are stored in a compact magazine, almost all machine-guns such as the GPMG and M60 are belt-fed. That gives them a high rate of fire, which is what you'll need to keep the enemy's heads down. But it also makes them hungry beasts, and the barrel needs frequent changing after heavy firing.

Every soldier needs to know the basics of field stripping, loading and using the machine-gun, and that means everything from laying down effective fire to extracting a jammed round or making up the link belt. If you can master the GPMG and how it works, you'll be everyone's mate. If you can't, you're going to be in trouble when the going gets tough.

1 Loading and making ready

The feed tray has to be released by catches in front of the rear sight before it can be lifted (A), in the right hand. The belt, in the left hand, is flipped over (B) into place. The cover is then closed (C) firmly. The sights are then set and, with the butt firmly in the shoulder, the cocking handle is pulled back (D). This pulls back the working parts (diagram, right). The gun can now be fired.

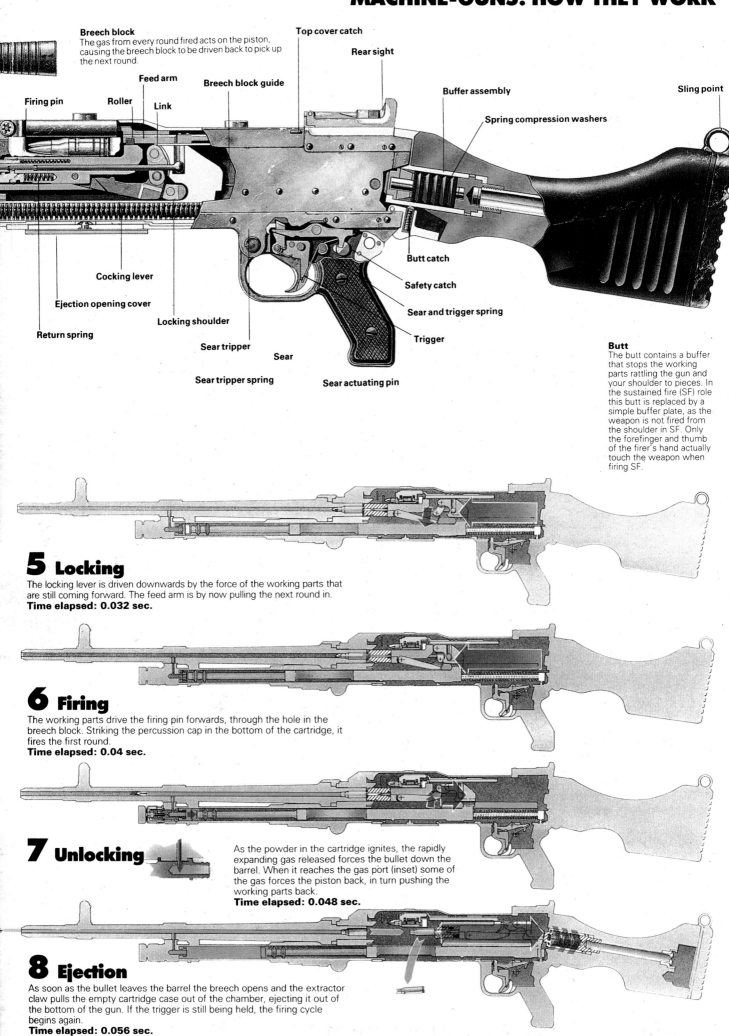

Breech block
The gas from every round fired acts on the piston, causing the breech block to be driven back to pick up the next round.

Top cover catch

Rear sight

Feed arm

Breech block guide

Buffer assembly

Sling point

Spring compression washers

Firing pin

Roller

Link

Cocking lever

Butt catch

Ejection opening cover

Safety catch

Locking shoulder

Sear and trigger spring

Return spring

Trigger

Sear tripper

Sear

Sear tripper spring

Sear actuating pin

Butt
The butt contains a buffer that stops the working parts rattling the gun and your shoulder to pieces. In the sustained fire (SF) role this butt is replaced by a simple buffer plate, as the weapon is not fired from the shoulder in SF. Only the forefinger and thumb of the firer's hand actually touch the weapon when firing SF.

5 Locking
The locking lever is driven downwards by the force of the working parts that are still coming forward. The feed arm is by now pulling the next round in.
Time elapsed: 0.032 sec.

6 Firing
The working parts drive the firing pin forwards, through the hole in the breech block. Striking the percussion cap in the bottom of the cartridge, it fires the first round.
Time elapsed: 0.04 sec.

7 Unlocking
As the powder in the cartridge ignites, the rapidly expanding gas released forces the bullet down the barrel. When it reaches the gas port (inset) some of the gas forces the piston back, in turn pushing the working parts back.
Time elapsed: 0.048 sec.

8 Ejection
As soon as the bullet leaves the barrel the breech opens and the extractor claw pulls the empty cartridge case out of the chamber, ejecting it out of the bottom of the gun. If the trigger is still being held, the firing cycle begins again.
Time elapsed: 0.056 sec.

M60 GPMG

The M60 is the standard squad GPMG of the US Army. Introduced in 1960, it became known as the 'Pig' by soldiers in Vietnam on account of its ugliness, unreliability, excessive weight, and hard-to-change barrel. Time, however, has ironed out most of these problems and the current M60E1 is a reliable and powerful weapon.

Action
The M60 is a gas-operated machine gun. Gas generated from firing is diverted into a gas cylinder below the barrel, this forcing back a piston which in turn operates the bolt. When the first round is loaded, pulling the trigger sends the bolt forward, stripping a round from the belt, chambering it, and locking the bolt in place through rotating lugs. The firing pin then detonates the cartridge and as the bullet passes the gas-port tube, the cycle begins again under the pressure of the gas piston.

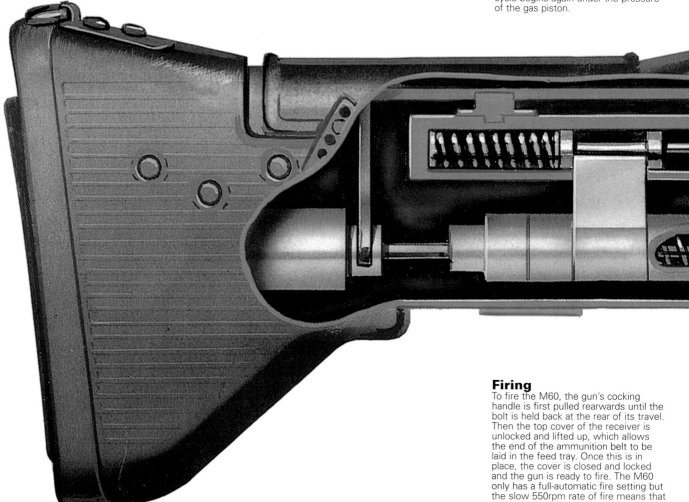

Firing
To fire the M60, the gun's cocking handle is first pulled rearwards until the bolt is held back at the rear of its travel. Then the top cover of the receiver is unlocked and lifted up, which allows the end of the ammunition belt to be laid in the feed tray. Once this is in place, the cover is closed and locked and the gun is ready to fire. The M60 only has a full-automatic fire setting but the slow 550rpm rate of fire means that single shots can be squeezed off.

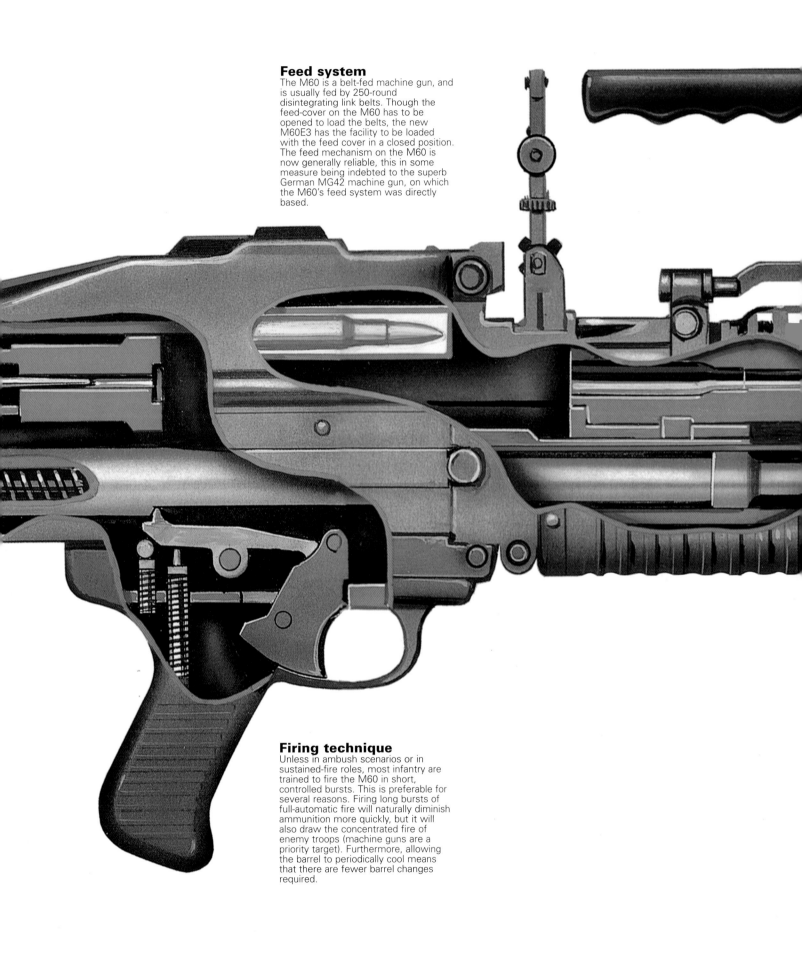

Feed system
The M60 is a belt-fed machine gun, and is usually fed by 250-round disintegrating link belts. Though the feed-cover on the M60 has to be opened to load the belts, the new M60E3 has the facility to be loaded with the feed cover in a closed position. The feed mechanism on the M60 is now generally reliable, this in some measure being indebted to the superb German MG42 machine gun, on which the M60's feed system was directly based.

Firing technique
Unless in ambush scenarios or in sustained-fire roles, most infantry are trained to fire the M60 in short, controlled bursts. This is preferable for several reasons. Firing long bursts of full-automatic fire will naturally diminish ammunition more quickly, but it will also draw the concentrated fire of enemy troops (machine guns are a priority target). Furthermore, allowing the barrel to periodically cool means that there are fewer barrel changes required.

The workings of the machine-gun

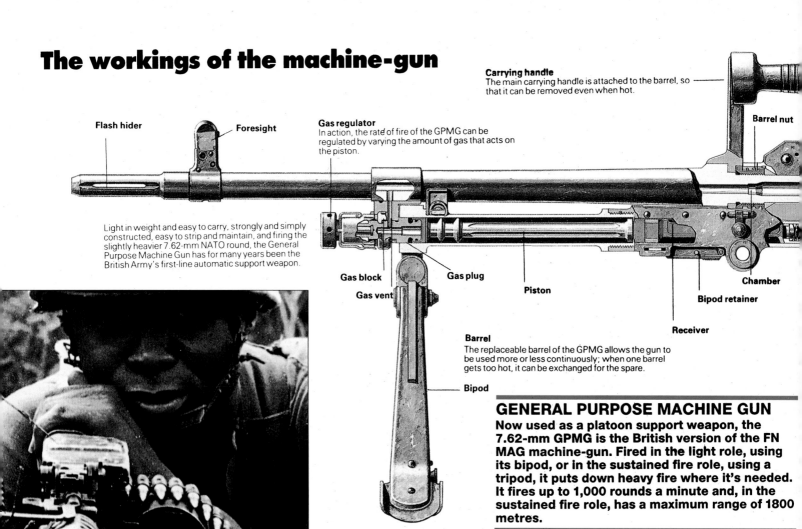

Carrying handle
The main carrying handle is attached to the barrel, so that it can be removed even when hot.

Flash hider

Foresight

Gas regulator
In action, the rate of fire of the GPMG can be regulated by varying the amount of gas that acts on the piston.

Barrel nut

Light in weight and easy to carry, strongly and simply constructed, easy to strip and maintain, and firing the slightly heavier 7.62-mm NATO round, the General Purpose Machine Gun has for many years been the British Army's first-line automatic support weapon.

Gas block

Gas plug

Gas vent

Piston

Chamber

Bipod retainer

Receiver

Barrel
The replaceable barrel of the GPMG allows the gun to be used more or less continuously; when one barrel gets too hot, it can be exchanged for the spare.

Bipod

GENERAL PURPOSE MACHINE GUN
Now used as a platoon support weapon, the 7.62-mm GPMG is the British version of the FN MAG machine-gun. Fired in the light role, using its bipod, or in the sustained fire role, using a tripod, it puts down heavy fire where it's needed. It fires up to 1,000 rounds a minute and, in the sustained fire role, has a maximum range of 1800 metres.

Left: In Vietnam, as in all other wars, soldiers made unofficial adaptations to their weapons. Here an M60 gunner has improved on the feed tray by strapping a C-ration can to the side of the gun. Most stoppages are caused by damaged or corroded ammunition, so anything that keeps it in good condition will help.

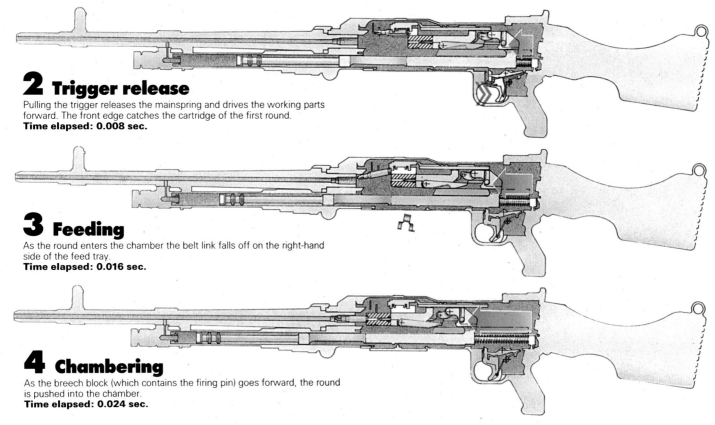

2 Trigger release
Pulling the trigger releases the mainspring and drives the working parts forward. The front edge catches the cartridge of the first round.
Time elapsed: 0.008 sec.

3 Feeding
As the round enters the chamber the belt link falls off on the right-hand side of the feed tray.
Time elapsed: 0.016 sec.

4 Chambering
As the breech block (which contains the firing pin) goes forward, the round is pushed into the chamber.
Time elapsed: 0.024 sec.

SUSTAINED FIREPOWER

Below: A German MG34 in the SF role on the Eastern Front during World War II. The man with the binoculars is the commander of the gun team.

Mounted on a tripod, a GPMG can be fired at targets up to 1800 metres away. A special sight allows the gun team to observe targets in daylight, record their location, and shoot at them with great accuracy at night or through a smokescreen.

A machine-gun firing from a stable platform produces a predictable pattern of fire. Fixed to a tripod, stamped into the ground and weighted down with sandbags, the GPMG is controlled by a dial sight. This allows the gun team to finely tune the elevation and bearing of the gun, making it as accurate as possible. The bullets will land in an area shaped like a fat cigar — up to 100 metres long and 50 metres wide. For this reason, gun teams try to position themselves to fire along a line of enemy troops rather than straight at them.

Barrel changing

The first M60s were meant to offer quick-change barrels, though this did not work in practice. The problem was that the barrel, the gas cylinder and even bipod were all one unit, and thus could not easily be removed or installed by one man (without the barrel the gun has no support during changing). Add to this a white-hot barrel and burns easily occurred (the M60 came supplied with an asbestos glove). The modern M60s now provide the barrel as a detached piece.

Sights
The M60's front sight is locked into a permanent position. This means that the operator zeros on the back sight alone. The problem is that with each barrel-change the zero setting changes with the new front sight. Unless the operator can remember the correct zero setting for each barrel – almost impossible – the same zero setting has to be used for all barrels, thus compromising the M60's accuracy.

Barrel life
Like most GPMGs, the standard M60 requires a barrel change about every two belts – based on each belt holding 250 rounds of 7.62-mm ammunition. However, the life of the M60's barrel has been improved on the M60E1. This version has a Stellite lining applied to the barrel and this gives a much improved durability over standard steel barrels, though the necessity to change a barrel is still dependent on the firing technique of the user.

Mounts
The standard M60 comes with a bipod mount. At first, the fact that the bipod was permanently attached to the barrel made it an unwelcome extra weight for the loader to carry. However, today lightweight bipods are fixed independently of the barrel. The M60 can also be placed on tripods or vehicle mounts and special forces units train themselves to fire the M60 from the hip – a considerably feat of strength.

Precision aiming with the

Above: This modern British *GPMG* is deployed with a *MILAN* missile launcher in the background.

Digging in for defence

GPMGs are an important defensive weapon and are ideally sited in pairs with an infantry section to provide close protection. Argentine machine-gun bunkers provided the most serious opposition to the British attacks on their positions outside Port Stanley during the Falklands war. They proved very difficult to shift: the simplest solution was to knock them out with MILAN anti-tank missiles.

Left: An Argentine machine-gun team is using the same basic *GPMG* as the British forces – a licence-built version of the Belgian *FN MAG*.

How to dig in a *GPMG*: note the overhead cover, which must be at least 50 cm thick to keep out enemy shell fragments.

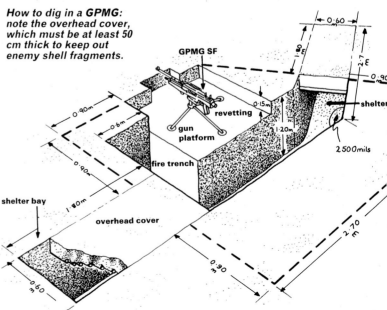

GPMG SF

revetting

gun platform

fire trench

shelter

2500 mils

shelter bay

overhead cover

C2 sight

British GPMGs are fitted with the C2 dial sight when deployed in the Sustained Fire role. By hammering an aiming post (a thin metal rod about 50 cm long) a few metres from the gun, the gun team gain a constant reference point for the machine-gun. The gun is lined up on the target and, looking through the telescope on the C2, the gunner can record the exact bearing to the aiming post. Then, at night or in fog, he can line up on the aiming post, which will leave the machine-gun pointing at the target he can no longer see.

Top left and above: The GPMG is shown with dial sight attached ready for an SF task. The total weight of the SF kit is over 36 kg and includes two extra barrels. These are changed every 400 rounds.

Right: The C2 allows the gun team to pre-register up to six different targets. The aiming post hammered into the ground near the gun contains a Trilux element which glows at night, allowing the machine-gun to operate in complete darkness.

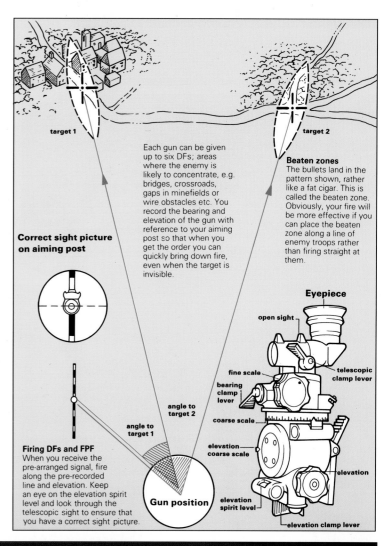

target 1

target 2

Correct sight picture on aiming post

Each gun can be given up to six DFs; areas where the enemy is likely to concentrate, e.g. bridges, crossroads, gaps in minefields or wire obstacles etc. You record the bearing and elevation of the gun with reference to your aiming post so that when you get the order you can quickly bring down fire, even when the target is invisible.

Beaten zones
The bullets land in the pattern shown, rather like a fat cigar. This is called the beaten zone. Obviously, your fire will be more effective if you can place the beaten zone along a line of enemy troops rather than firing straight at them.

Eyepiece

open sight

fine scale

telescopic clamp lever

bearing clamp lever

coarse scale

elevation coarse scale

elevation

angle to target 2

angle to target 1

elevation spirit level

Gun position

elevation clamp lever

Firing DFs and FPF
When you receive the pre-arranged signal, fire along the pre-recorded line and elevation. Keep an eye on the elevation spirit level and look through the telescopic sight to ensure that you have a correct sight picture.

The lethal zone

At ranges up to 600 metres, the bullets from a GPMG travel in a straight line. Firing over flat ground, the bullets travel parallel to the earth and can hit anyone within range. But the gun must be elevated to reach targets at longer ranges. The bullets travel along a curved path so someone close to the gun is relatively safe: the rounds will pass overhead. Eventually the bullets drop low enough to strike a standing target. This is known as 'first catch'. A little further on, they hit the ground: this is called 'first graze'.

A hail of red tracer from a British GPMG lights up the night. The tracer element burns out at 1100 metres, but if a gunner can observe the bullet strike he can fire to the weapon's maximum range, 1800 metres.

Although the machine-gun is secured to a firmly anchored tripod, the bullets will not all land in the same place. The smallest movement of the gun will affect the path of the bullets, and minute variations in the bullets themselves can make a big difference in long-range shooting. But the shape and size of the area swept by the GPMG's bullets can be accurately predicted.

Machine-guns will fire their rounds into an area of predictable size called the beaten zone. Since it is easier to avoid lateral error than vertical, the beaten zone will be deeper than it is wide.

Dangerous space is the full distance between first catch (where bullets are low enough to strike the top of the target) and first graze, the first point at which they strike the ground.

first catch

first graze

dangerous space

beaten zone

danger zone

500 metres

Range 500 metres: beaten zone produced by a GPMG is 1m wide and 110m long

Maximum damage
Firing over flat ground at 600 metres, a machine-gun will fire on a flat trajectory so the dangerous space will extend from the muzzle of the gun out top the beginning of the beaten zone.

Increasing the range
As the range increases, the rounds must rise higher in order to reach the target and the beaten zone will become shorter and wider.

Range 1000 metres: beaten zone is 2m wide and 75m long

1000 metres

The M60

EYE WITNESS

"We lifted off and headed over the South China Sea. Once over the water, we loaded our M60s and test-fired them to make sure they were working. I was glad for this practice, especially since the time I put the gas piston in backwards. Meanwhile Major Burrow was test-firing the rockets and four M60 machine-guns. We climbed to about 1,500ft, then nosed into a gradual dive. When we were at about 900ft and close to the target area, the major said, 'Let her rip!'

"I jerked the trigger on my M60 and kept the tracers streaking for the hedgerow. Two gooks jumped away and I got them. Another one ran out of the hedgerow and headed for some thicker cover. I followed him with my tracers until he disappeared, probably by diving into a hole. As we crossed over the hedgerow, I stepped out on the rocket pod and turned the M60 to the rear to cover the backside of the bird. All I could see were big columns of grey smoke rolling up to the sky. I fired until the machine-gun ran out of ammo."

Sergeant Jim Black, door gunner, 1/9th Cavalry, US Army 1967-8

Main pic: A US Marine Corps M60 team fires on North Vietnamese positions during the battle for Hue City in 1968. The NVA recognised the importance of the M60s and concentrated their fire on the American gun teams.

A US Marine M60 gunner describes a typical night ambush in Vietnam.

"Sweat dripped off my palms. I tried unbuttoning the holster of my .45-calibre pistol. My hands felt shaky, almost spastic.

"Chan nudged me and squinted. 'You don't think they're getting that close?'

"'I sure hope not. I don't think this sucker works.'

"We gave each other a quick, hard look. The realisation of what we just said sank in.

Taking aims

"The four shadows turned into four men 50 metres away and closing. I followed the lead man with my gun sights, making sure my finger stayed off the trigger. One early

NAM

point crept by like they were stepping on unbroken eggs. The moon silhouetted their safari helmets. NVA regulars.

"The moon bathed the landscape in an eerie blue light. Chan held the first 15 inches of the ammo belt in his left hand with his M16 rammed into his right shoulder.

Enemy approach

"The four NVA walking point were within 20 metres of our line of riflemen, and the column was still filing out of the brush at the foot of the mountains. The usual chatter of the jungle insects vanished.

"Chan released his rifle and reached into one of his huge trouser pockets, producing a small can of oil. He began squeezing it onto the

barrel of the M60 as he whispered so low I only heard two words: '. . .whole company.'

"Shadows kept multiplying from the foot of the mountains. Every other man in the column was bent over to the waist, lumbering under the weight of huge packs. The men in between the carriers walked more upright, with smaller packs, and carried rifles. I had a human supply train in front of me. This would be payback, long-awaited payback.

"My stomach still churned. In a few seconds I'd kill a lot of people. My stomach bellowed loudly, then rumbled with more than enough noise to carry to Hanoi. A brackish taste filled my mouth. I wanted to spit, but there wasn't any saliva.

Left: The versatile M60 became the main armament of US Army helicopters in Vietnam. This Huey has four M60s in a fixed forward-firing mount.

Left: An M60 gunner opens fire as his assistant feeds the fresh belt into the weapon. Contact with the Viet Cong would lead to the shout 'Guns Up!' and the M60 teams would rush into firing positions to suppress the enemy.

Right: In addition to the quadruple M60 mounting, the helicopter retains the standard M60 'door gun' used by troop carrying Hueys to provide covering fire on the Landing Zones. The huge quantities of ammunition expended in this way led to the calculation that over a million bullets were fired for every enemy killed.

finger could get us all killed.

"From the corner of my eye, more movement. More shadows. Stinging salt sweat penetrated my eyes. The line of shadows grew longer. My bladder felt like exploding.

"Twenty metres in front, crouching down and looking in all directions, the four gooks walking

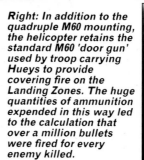

Left: The helicopter's M60s fire on Viet Cong positions along a river bank. 'Walking' fire on to a target was a technique used by M60 gunners on the ground and in the air alike. Using tracer rounds helped the gunner spot where he was hitting, but they also betrayed his exact location.

Left: An Australian M60 machine-gunner fords a stream in Vietnam. The men following him are armed with 7.62-mm FN FAL rifles so, unlike the Americans, everyone in the section is using the same ammunition.

"Doubt strangled me. Fifteen of us were about to ambush a column of gooks I couldn't see the end of. A quick violent shiver shot from my neck to the base of my spine.

"*Bloop.* Sam's blooper gun! I pulled the trigger. Orange tracers spiralled away from me. My first target exploded backward, arms and legs flailing. I laid on the trigger for what seemed like eternity. Frantic screams screeched from the rice paddy, piercing even the explosions. I could feel the screams more than I could hear them. The NVA scrambled for cover that wasn't there. Some ran from the machine-gun fire and directly into the row of M16s, while those at the front of the column retreated into a shower of lead from the M60. The crossfire was a human lawn mower.

"I swept the machine-gun from one end of the column to the bottom of the mountains. The phosphorus ends of the tracer rounds broke off the bullets and sizzled like miniature sparklers as they found their mark.

"Chan changed clips in his rifle as fast as he could. The barrel of the M60 glowed red, then white. Adrenalin and fear pushed me, while my whole body vibrated to the rhythm of the gun; I became one with my weapon, and we were killing. The barrel became transparent from the heat of continuous fire as I poured another hundred rounds into the rice paddy.

Glowing barrel

"A fluorescent lamp couldn't have pinpointed my position any better than that glowing barrel. I knew the barrel might melt and jam, but I couldn't stop. I felt like I did in my first fistfight, scared to stop swinging for fear of getting hit.

"Chan dropped his rifle and started frantically feeding ammo into the gun with both hands. Sam's M79 blooper-round explosions sounded consistent, almost automatic. His speed was phenomenal.

Left: M60 armed US Marines are shown aboard the merchant ship SS Mayaguez after they recaptured the vessel from the Cambodians.

Above: A classic shot of a US Army M60 gunner. Balanced on the tree trunk, the gun is in a poor position for accurate fire and the heap of 7.62-mm ammunition is piled up for the benefit of the cameraman.

Above: A US Marine Corps M60 team in action near the so-called 'De-Militarized Zone': the border between North and South Vietnam.

"Louder, more powerful explosions of grenades and ChiComs sporadically thundered above the blooper rounds. The speedy bursts of M16 fire mingled with the slower, more powerful cracking of AK fire in a chorus of insane chaos.

NVA fire

"Total confusion engulfed the rice paddy. A few NVA fired back. Others dragged dead and wounded toward the safety of the mountains. A flare sizzled into the dark sky, arcing over the paddy, then popping into a tiny sun and drifting down. The lights were on. The miniature red sun added a 3-D effect to an already bloody picture.

"Chan screamed and reached for his rifle. Three gooks were running at us, bobbing and weaving in a suicidal charge to knock out the gun. They fired full automatic, spraying bullets all around us. They were screaming. I swept the stream of tracers from left to right, bearing down on them like a sputtering laser beam. A ChiCom grenade blew up 10 feet in front of us, stealing my night vision with a white explosion. Incoming bullets kicked dirt into my eyes and mouth. The barrel melted. The gun jammed. The sweeping laser

stopped along with my breathing.

"I fumbled for my pistol like a drunk in a shoot-out. My vision turned spotty. I heard Chan firing. The grunts on my left opened up full automatic. Blurred images of two men 10 metres away came through the spots in my eyes. Their heads jerked back like poorly manned puppets, legs crumbling last, not knowing the upper half was lifeless.

"Silence. The loudest silence of my life. My heart pounded the breath out of me faster than I could bring it in. The bloodlust evaporated into the gunpowder air. Pay back. The frustration turned into fatigue. . . 'Chan. . . Are you hit?'

"'No. Are you?' he asked.

"'No. I'll be okay when I see the sun.'

"'Praise the Lord,' whispered Chan.

"The night became deathly still. The moon slid behind thick, dark rain clouds. The sting of ants and mosquitoes returned. I felt like talking to Chan, but I knew better

than to relax now. I leaned against my pack and stared into the rice paddy.

"Dawn finally came, lifting pressure from me with each inch of the yellow sun peeking up behind us. The first movement came from the chief. He moved smoothly from position to position until he made his way to us. He looked to be always in perfect balance.

Body count

"'We're going out for a body count. Keep us covered.' He turned to the tree line and gave a wave. As the chief started into the paddy, Doyle and Striker came out of the tree line with their rifles on their hips. Swift Eagle stopped. He looked over his shoulder at Chan and me. He gave a nod and a thumbs up.

"'You did good.' His stoic face showed the same expression it always did – none; but his piercing black eyes left no doubt. We had just gotten the seal of approval. We were salts. Old salts.

The General Purpose Machine Gun (GPMG) has been adopted by over 80 countries, such are its qualities. It can fire 250 rounds of 7.62-mm ammunition in less than 25 seconds, each round with a killing force of up to a mile.

A US soldier prepares to fire an M249 Squad Automatic Weapon (SAW). The SAW uses the same 5.56-mm NATO round as the M16 rifle, and has feed options of either a 30-round box or 200-round belt.

Modern Light
MACHINE-GUNS

This US Army Ranger is armed with the 5.56-mm SAW (Squad Automatic Weapon). Firing the same ammunition as the rest of the squad's M16A2 rifles, the SAW is used to suppress enemy positions with accurate automatic fire.

Light machine-guns are the primary weapon of the smallest infantry unit, the 8-10 man section. With the same ammo and a longer effective range than standard assault rifles and superior automatic fire capability yet lighter than the GPMG, LMGs are vital weapons.

The sniper had them pinned down now. From his position high on the mountainside he could pick off the paratroops one by one. Their BMD armoured personnel carrier had hit a mine on a dusty track near Jalalabad. The guerrillas were a good 500 metres away, beyond the effective range of the Soviets' AK-74 assault rifles, letting their sniper finish them at leisure.

Senior sergeant Platov laid down his rifle and dived back inside the upturned vehicle. Petrol flowed freely over the hot metal inside. He seized the machine-gun by its barrel and tugged it from the dead hands of its owner. Bullets smacked into the road and clanged against the armoured skin of the BMD. Leaping back to the roadside, he flipped the bipod down and took careful aim. His first round went left, the second struck low, then a short burst scattered rock fragments into the air around the Afghans' position. The RPK-74 light machine-gun soon persuaded the guerrillas to seek an easier target.

81

The RPK-74 looks very similar to the current Russian assault rifle. But its barrel is over half as long again and it is supported by a bipod which folds up under the barrel when not in use. Firing from a 40- instead of a 30-round magazine, it is one of several weapons issued to the Russian infantry to tackle targets outside the effective range of their rifles. It cannot pump out rounds in the same fashion as a belt-fed machine-gun because the barrel cannot be changed. Continued firing will heat it rapidly until the weapon malfunctions. However, the barrel is heavier than on the standard rifle, and the formidable strength of Russian weapons allows it to put down a lot of rounds when the situation demands.

Firing short bursts

The combination of the bipod and longer barrel makes it far more accurate than the rifle. Firing short bursts, it is used to suppress enemy positions the Soviets are assaulting or to mow down attacking infantry. Experienced soldiers can squeeze off single rounds to engage targets at much longer range.

The different categories of 'light',

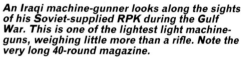
An Iraqi machine-gunner looks along the sights of his Soviet-supplied RPK during the Gulf War. This is one of the lightest light machine-guns, weighing little more than a rifle. Note the very long 40-round magazine.

FLASHBACK
French troops demonstrate the 'assault fire' technique developed for the Chauchat LMG.

The world's worst machine-gun

The Chauchat light machine-gun entered service with the French army during 1915. Although the French soldiers were among the first to develop modern tactics of fire and manoeuvre, they were handicapped from the start by its poor design. Its mechanical operation was not suited to such a weapon since it caused considerable movement inside the gun, making a steady firing position all but impossible. It was manufactured with poor-quality materials with equally bad quality control. The result was a weapon that suffered frequent malfunctions. It was difficult to clear a stoppage, and many problems could only be dealt with by a unit armourer in his workshop. Not much good for a soldier fighting in a front-line trench. The Chauchat is widely recognised as the worst-designed light machine-gun ever to enter service.

'medium', 'heavy' and 'general-purpose' machine-guns were introduced as new weapons were developed. A century after the machine-gun entered widespread service, the classifications overlap in many cases. The term light machine-gun is used to describe a machine-gun which can be carried and operated by one man alone. Bigger machine-guns, operated by a crew and generally mounted on a tripod were termed 'medium' or 'heavy' machine-guns during World War II depending on the type of ammunition they fired. Medium machine-guns generally fired the same calibre ammunition as service rifles. Heavy machine-guns fired 12.7-mm (.5-in) or larger cartridges

MODERN LIGHT MACHINE-GUNS Reference File

197
SPAIN

5.56-mm CETME Ameli assault weapon

The Spanish **Ameli** 'assault machine-gun' is a far cry from the old-style light machine-guns typified by the British L4 Bren gun. Unlike most 'light' machine-guns, the Ameli actually lives up to the description and it was quickly adopted by Spain's specialist anti-terrorist unit. As all NATO armies moved to adopt the 5.56-mm rifle cartridge during the 1980s, it was obvious that many forces would want to change their machine-guns to use the same ammunition. Although the Americans got away with it in Vietnam, having 7.62-mm machine-guns in infantry squads using 5.56-mm calibre rifles is a logistical nightmare. CETME moved quickly to fill the gap.

The Ameli bears more than a passing resemblance to the famous World War

II German MG42 general-purpose machine-gun. CETME built its post-war reputation on the German roller-locking system and produced a version of the MG42 under licence. The Ameli is a scaled-down version with a number of improvements. It is carefully designed to be as 'idiot-proof' as possible: easy to strip down, very reliable and extremely safe. Its high cyclic rate continues the German philosophy of using a hail of fire to suppress targets, but the Ameli's low recoil makes it impressively accurate as well. The title 'assault weapon' comes from the fact that the Ameli can not only be fired from the hip, but from the shoulder too. In a close-range gun battle, the Ameli is closer to an assault rifle than an LMG.

Specification
Ameli 5.56-mm assault weapon
Cartridge: 5.56-mm×45 NATO
Feed: disintegrating link or box
Weight: 5.7 kg with bipod
Length: 970 mm overall
Barrel length: 400 mm
Cyclic rate of fire: 850-950 rpm

Looking very like the World War II German MG42 machine-gun, the Ameli is light enough to be used as an assault weapon. Even with 200 rounds loaded, it is lighter than the British 7.62-mm GPMG.

Below: The M249 SAW is one of several light machine-guns which can fire from belts of ammunition rather than box magazines.

Above: An observation post set up by the Royal Marines is equipped with an M79 40-mm grenade-launcher and an L4 light machine-gun for defence. Note the camera with telephoto lens.

and were the only weapons to do so until the advent of the American .50-in sniper rifles.

General Purpose Machine Guns

These classifications were blurred during the 1930s when Germany introduced the 'general-purpose' machine-gun. The MG34 and MG42 could be carried and fired by one man. But they could also be fitted to a bipod and fed from belted ammunition. Their barrels could be quickly changed so they could maintain a sustained fire of several hundred rounds per minute.

But light machine-guns soldiered on. In World War I, the British Army used the American-designed Lewis gun. From 1915 the .303-in Vickers guns were withdrawn from the infantry battalions and grouped together

198

BELGIUM

FN Minimi light machine-gun

Since 1984 the US Army has been replacing one M16 rifle in each infantry squad with a Belgian light machine-gun, the **Minimi**. Under the designation M249 Squad Automatic Weapon, it provides American rifle squads with formidable firepower beyond the effective range of their M16s. Experience in Vietnam led the US Army to demand a new automatic weapon for its infantry, able to chew through steel helmets at 800 metres, yet light enough to be operated by one soldier alone. The Fabrique National design won the competition conducted by the Army and it is a very cost-effective weapon: the US Army was paying less than $4,000 each in the mid-1980s.

Using tried and tested mechanical

Fabrique National's Minimi has proved a major success for the Belgian firm. Adopted by the US Army, it supplements the larger M60 7.62-mm machine-guns.

systems, the M249 relies on a conventional bolt and gas piston arrangement with adjustable gas pressure. It is fed by disintegrating link, standard M16 rifle magazines, or 200-round belts that arrive in sturdy plastic cans that clamp straight on to the gun. This helps to keep out mud and dirt and reduces the overall weight. It is another soldier-proof design, field stripped without tools and with no catches or pins to drop off into the grass, never to

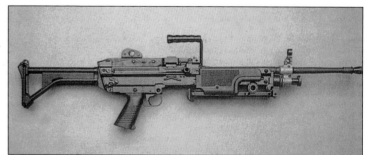

be seen again. Its accuracy compares very favourably with conventional 7.62-mm machine-guns like the old M60.

Specification
5.56-mm Minimi
Cartridge: 5.56-mm×45 NATO
Feed: disintegrating link or M16 rifle magazines
Weight: 10 kg with 200-round box magazine
Length: 1040 mm
Barrel length: 466 mm
Cyclic rate of fire: 750-1000 rounds per minute

in the Machine-Gun Corps. Thus the infantry came to rely on their Lewis guns to provide the bulk of their firepower. Although eventually described as a light machine-gun since they were capable of being operated by one man, they were normally handled by a 10-man section. This was mainly because of the quantity of ammunition needed – the section carried 44 of the 47-round drum magazines: 2,068 rounds which weighed 82.5 kg alone.

During the 1930s each British infantry section became the equivalent of a Lewis gun section as the Czech-designed Bren gun was adopted. This light machine-gun was regarded as the principle weapon of the section, the fire of the riflemen was supplementary.

---

199   SINGAPORE

Ultimax 100 5.56-mm light machine-gun

Chartered Industries of Singapore produces a range of military hardware designed for the cost-conscious Third World army. The **Ultimax** follows the same philosophy as the Ameli: a light assault weapon that is nearer to a heavy rifle than a machine-gun, but retaining the ability to deliver sustained fire unlike the Russian RPK. Its appearance is not over-impressive; the quality of manufacture compares poorly with the Ameli or Minimi. But there is no doubting its light weight, even with the 100-round drum magazine attached.

The Ultimax is designed to manage the roughest of conditions, wide tolerances inside and a gas pressure regulator allow the gun to keep functioning even with dirt and fouling

inside. It is easily field-stripped, with no tools necessary and no small parts to get lost in the process. The barrel has a quick-change facility allowing sustained fire. In the assault role, it performs equally well since recoil is very low. The Ultimax can be fired without its butt stock and a shorter barrel is available for airborne troops who want a smaller, more portable weapon.

Specification
5.56-mm Ultimax
Cartridge: 5.56-mm×45 NATO
Feed: 100-round drum or 20- or 30-round box magazines
Weight: 6.5 kg with 100-round magazine, bipod and sling
Length: 1030 mm

Barrel length: 508 mm
Cyclic rate of fire: 500-540 rounds per minute

Adopted by the Singapore armed forces, the Ultimax has been supplemented by 7.62-mm and 12.7-mm weapons as part of a package being promoted worldwide.

---

200   AUSTRIA

5.56-mm Steyr light support weapon

The famous **Steyr AUG** (Army Universal Gun) is a complete weapons' system. The rifle has been adopted by Austria, Australia, Oman, the Irish Republic and others. This light support weapon is a heavy-barrelled version of the rifle and its basic operation is identical. It is manufactured in several models. The basic LMG retains the carrying handle and optical sight fitted to the AUG rifle. The LMG-T has a different receiver assembly which includes a flat bar mount for a more powerful telescopic sight or night vision system. Both are fitted with a flash hider which also reduces muzzle climb.

Like all members of the AUG family, the LMG feeds from a translucent plastic magazine. This is a major

Like the British SA80 rifle, Steyr's AUG has a heavy barrel version that serves as a light support weapon. It comes in two versions, both with telescopic sights.

advance. The soldier can quickly see how many rounds he has remaining, and the plastic lips of the magazine do not dent or bend like cheap metal ones – a frequent cause of malfunctions. Like the British SA80, the AUG uses a bullpup configuration to reduce the overall length. Unlike the British weapon, the AUG has an enviable reputation for reliability under the most arduous conditions.

Specification
5.56-mm Steyr AUG LMG
Cartridge: 5.56-mm×45 NATO
Feed: 30- or 42-round plastic magazine
Weight: 5.4 kg with 30-round magazine

Length: 900 mm
Barrel length: 621 mm
Cyclic rate of fire: 680 rounds per minute

Below: Lying behind a convenient bank, this British soldier does not need the bipod of his LSW, which remains folded under the barrel.

Each rifleman carried ammunition for the Bren gun and all riflemen were supposed to be capable of operating the Bren gun. Tactics were built around the fire and manoeuvre of the 'gun group' – the Bren gun and three soldiers – plus the 'rifle group' – six private soldiers led by their Corporal.

Easier to learn

After World War II the idea of the general-purpose machine-gun was taken up by all armies. It made obvious sense to use a multi-purpose weapon since soldiers only had to learn how to use one machine-gun. World War I-style medium machine-guns like the Vickers took a long time to learn how to use. They could not be taken over in an emergency nor fired with much success by soldiers unfamiliar with them.

Despite the British Army's adoption of the Belgian FN MAG general-purpose machine-gun, the Bren gun continued in service. Modified to fire 7.62-mm NATO cartridges instead of the old .303-in round, the L4 was retained for operations where the heavy weight of fire provided by the GPMG was unlikely to be necessary; and where a lighter, handier

Wielding the Ultimax 100 like a rifle, a paratrooper of the Singapore armed forces demonstrates the weapon's easy handling characteristics. The drum magazine holds 100 rounds.

201

Royal Ordnance Light Support Weapon

This is the British equivalent of the Austrian Steyr AUG light machine-gun and the Russian RPK-74: a heavy-barreled version of the current service rifle, which any rifleman in a section could use if the gunner were wounded or killed. The long strip of what looks like Meccano protecting the barrel and the bipod immediately distinguish the **LSW** from the SA80 rifle. It also has an extra handle positioned behind the magazine. It is fitted with the same x4 magnification SUSAT sight which is a great aid to accurate shooting, particularly in poor light conditions.

The LSW is about as accurate as a 5.56-mm weapon can be – the effective range of this light cartridge is not much greater than 500 metres –

although a good shot can do better on a target range. Current manuals talk about effective fire at up to 800 metres, but a stiff wind will force the gunner to 'aim off' dramatically to allow for the wind blowing the bullet off course. The LSW has been affected by the same problems as the controversial SA80 rifle. While a few regiments have been very pleased with the new weapons, others have found them badly made and hopelessly unreliable.

Specification
5.56-mm Light Support Weapon
Cartridge: 5.56-mm×45 NATO
Feed: 30-round detachable box
Weight: 6.88 kg

Length: 900 mm
Barrel length: 638 mm
Cyclic rate of fire: 650-800 rounds per minute

The British Light Support Weapon is issued on a scale of two per infantry section. Using a light machine-gun that is closely based on a rifle design greatly simplifies training.

202

Galil ARM

The Israeli Galil rifle series includes rifles, machine-guns and shortened assault rifles similar to the Colt CAR-15. Closely modelled on the Soviet Kalashnikov rifle, the **Galil** is available in both 5.56-mm and 7.62-mm calibres. Battlefield performance is as impressive as their quality of manufacture. A robust folding stock makes for a handier weapon in the confines of a helicopter or armoured personnel carrier. The bipod fits into a groove under the foregrip when not in use; as the legs swing down they can also double as a wire-cutter.

The Galil ARM can be fired on semi or fully automatic. Firing single shots it is impressively accurate and the fire selector can be operated from either

Right: The Israeli's home-grown Galil rifle family includes weapons chambered for both 5.56-mm and 7.62-mm. One of the finest infantry weapons available, the Galil is closely based on the Russian Kalashnikov design.

side of the weapon. The cocking handle is attached to the bolt carrier so it can be positively closed if necessary. The change lever is similar to the AK-47: a long bar which prevents the carrier moving fully forward when on 'safe', but will allow enough retraction to let the soldier check that the chamber is clear.

Specification
5.56-mm Galil ARM
Cartridge: 5.56-mm×45 NATO
Feed: 35- or 50-round magazine
Weight: 4.91 kg with 35-round magazine

Length: 979 mm
Barrel length: 460 mm
Cyclic rate of fire: 650 rounds per minute

Combat Comparison

Light machine-guns based on rifle designs are usually not quite as flexible as weapons designed as machine-guns from the outset.

weapon was more appropriate. The L4 is still used in Norway by British units serving there, and has seen action in areas as diverse as Borneo and Northern Ireland.

The Soviet army completed its victorious progress from Moscow to Berlin armed with a wide variety of weapons. It soon standardised on the famous Kalashnikov rifle and adopted the RPD light machine-gun as the new squad automatic weapon. This feeds from a belt which is normally coiled inside a drum to make it easier to carry. The RPD was supplied in large numbers to North Vietnam and it was issued to most of their infantry squads.

The Soviets followed the trend towards GPMGs by fielding the 7.62-mm PK, but, in the early 1960s, their infantry sections were issued with a heavy-barrelled version of the AK rifle. Designated RPK, one was provided for each section in addition to its PK general-purpose machine-gun. Unlike the PK, the RPK uses the same ammunition as the Kalashnikov rifle and anyone trained on an AKM has no trouble operating the RPK. The RPK-74 is the latest version: a light machine-gun model of the AK-74 assault rifle which fires the 5.45-mm cartridge.

The Soviets' adoption of this smaller calibre paralleled the decision of most NATO armies to switch to 5.56-mm rifles instead of the 7.62-mm weapons in service since the 1950s. The British Army's controversial SA80 is

The trend towards 5.56-mm calibre light machine-guns has not been universally followed. Training to fight in the open bush where very long-range shooting can occur, the South African Defence Force retains full-power 7.62-mm machine-guns.

complemented by the LSW (Light Support Weapon). Like the RPK it is much the same as the rifle, but has a longer and heavier barrel supported by a bipod.

The US Army and Marine Corps have adopted the Belgian 5.56-mm Minimi under the designation SAW (Squad Automatic Weapon). This enables infantry squads to engage targets beyond the 400-500 metre effective range of their M16 rifles. It is obviously an advantage for a section's machine-gun to use the same ammunition as its rifles – so the light machine-gun is enjoying a new lease of life.

In many armies, the GPMGs which once looked like replacing them are being concentrated in specialist weapons' platoons. Although some new light machine-guns like the Spanish Ameli look like scaled-down GPMGs, they are designed to double as assault weapons. Just light enough to be fired from the shoulder by the determined soldier, the Ameli is ideal for Special Forces' teams that demand the heaviest firepower but cannot lug around a full-size GPMG. Light machine-guns remain a vital weapon for the modern infantryman.

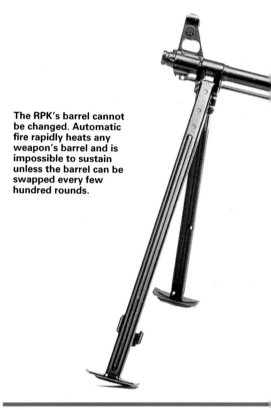

The RPK's barrel cannot be changed. Automatic fire rapidly heats any weapon's barrel and is impossible to sustain unless the barrel can be swapped every few hundred rounds.

The L4 is the last version of the Bren gun, first adopted in 1937 and still in service with the British Army. Its barrel can be changed quickly and easily, making it far more suited to prolonged action than the RPK.

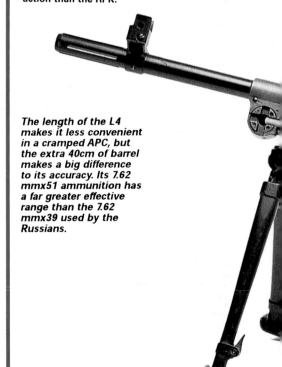

The length of the L4 makes it less convenient in a cramped APC, but the extra 40cm of barrel makes a big difference to its accuracy. Its 7.62 mmx51 ammunition has a far greater effective range than the 7.62 mmx39 used by the Russians.

In environments where weight is at a premium, the L4 7.62-mm machine-gun often replaced the GPMG in British service. This Royal Marine ski patrol is on exercise in northern Norway. Note how the weapons' shapes are disguised with black and white tape.

203

Former USSR

RPK light machine-guns

The RPK-74 is the current light machine-gun issued to Russian Motor Rifle and Airborne infantry. It is simply an AK-74 rifle with a heavier and longer barrel. The original RPK introduced in the early 1960s, is a similarly modified version of the AKM assault rifle. This fires the 7.62-mm×39 Soviet rifle cartridge and uses either the ordinary rifle magazines or a 40-round 'banana'

magazine of its own. It is also issued with a 75-round drum magazine, but since the barrel cannot be changed, sustained fire is out of the question.

The RPK series of light machine-guns is used to provide rather more-accurate fire than the average conscript rifleman is capable of. They are not able to deliver the sort of hail of lead that the Belgian Minimi or Spanish Ameli can produce. But since their basic operation is identical to that of the Kalashnikov rifles,

anyone trained on an AK will have no problem using an RPK. This is an obvious advantage over the Americans: US troops use three completely different types of firearms within each rifle platoon.

Specification
RPK 7.62-mm machine-gun
Cartridge: 7.62-mm×39
Feed: 75-, 40-round or standard 30-round rifle magazines
Weight: 5 kg
Length: 1035 mm
Barrel length: 591 mm
Cyclic rate of fire: 660 rounds per minute

The 40-round 'banana' magazine of the RPK is the most common, but 75-round drum magazines can be fitted before an assault so that the gunner does not have to pause to re-load at a vital moment.

The RPK's sights allow it to shoot at ranges up to 800 metres, although the limitations of its ammunition make it much less accurate over about 500 metres.

Light machine-guns are more accurate than assault rifles because they have longer barrels and are supported by a bipod. This gives a consistent and stable firing position, allowing short bursts to be delivered accurately.

204

UNITED KINGDOM

L4 Bren gun

The famous Bren gun used by British forces in World War II still soldiers on in the shape of the L4 7.62-mm machine-gun. When the 7.62-mm Self-Loading Rifle was adopted in the 1950s, Bren guns were modified to fire the new cartridge. Although the Fabrique National MAG was soon issued to British rifle sections as the

GPMG, the Bren gun was retained for several specialist roles. Much lighter than the GPMG, it was a more sensible choice for theatres of operation where weight was a prime consideration. In the jungles of Asia and Central America, plus the frozen wastes of northern Norway, the L4 Bren gun has continued in service.

Like its World War II predecessor, the L4 can be exceptionally accurate when firing single shots. Its box magazines restrict its ability to lay down sustained fire, but mechanical reliability is generally impressive, and the barrel can be quickly changed, unlike the Russian RPK series. If the situation calls for it, the L4 can produce 120 rounds a minute, although the barrel will need changing every 150 seconds. This is comparable with a GPMG if you have the magazines and spare barrels available.

Specification
7.62-mm L4A4 light machine-gun
Cartridge: 7.62-mm NATO
Feed: 30-round box magazine
Weight: 10 kg
Length: 1156 mm
Barrel length: 635 mm
Cyclic rate of fire: 500 rounds per minute

The L4 has an almost straight magazine instead of the familiar curved one associated with the original Bren gun. The old magazine's profile was dictated by the shape of the British .303-in rimmed rifle bullet.

LIGHT BUT LETHAL

Above: Royal Marines stand to in their defensive positions in Norway during an exercise. They retained the L4 light machine-gun, the last version of the Bren gun, because it was lighter and handier than the GPMG.

Light machine-guns provide the infantry with vital extra firepower in both attack and defence. With a longer effective range than rifles and the ability to deliver a heavier concentration of automatic fire, they have been the infantry section's primary weapon for 75 years.

To win an infantry firefight, one side must prevent most of the enemy soldiers from shooting effectively. Unless the enemy are hopelessly badly trained, it will be difficult to actually kill them. Instead, a combination of near misses and the sheer volume of bullets striking around them will persuade the enemy soldiers to stay behind their cover. Fewer and fewer of them will risk exposing themselves by trying to shoot back. Light machine-guns play a vital role in achieving this.

With their ability to deliver accurate automatic fire, LMGs can pin down the enemy. With most of the enemy remaining in cover, an attacker is free to manoeuvre forward and eventually to assault the position with grenades and even

the bayonet. Successful use of the LMG is often the key to achieving fire superiority and thus victory.

This was obviously true until the end of World War II, when most riflemen were equipped with bolt-action rifles incapable of automatic fire. It has remained true because few assault rifles can match the light machine-gun's accuracy when firing fully automatic. As 7.62-mm rifles are replaced by 5.56-mm weapons like the SA80, the number of LMGs is increasing. The British Army's eight-10 man infantry sections built around an LMG (or GPMG in the light role) are now split into two four-man 'fire teams'. Each has a 5.56-mm Light Support Weapon (LSW) and three riflemen. The light machine-gun is still in business.

The legend of the Bren Gun

From the North African desert to the hedgerows of Normandy and the Burmese jungle, the Bren gun was the primary weapon of the British infantry section during World War II. This Czechoslovakian weapon was adopted in 1937 and a version is still in service over 50 years later. The 3-5 round bursts from the Bren may not have sounded as impressive as the German MG42, which could shoot twice as fast, but its accuracy is exceptional, whether firing single shots or the regulation short bursts. Its simplicity and strength of construction make it easy to operate and maintain. It remains the best light machine-gun ever designed.

Right: A Bren gun in action during World War II. The distinctively curved shape of the magazine was necessary since the British .303-in rifle cartridge had a rim at its base, unlike the original Czech design, which used the rimless German 7.92-mm round.

This British patrol, seen in Northern Ireland during the 1980s, relies on a 7.62-mm L4 light machine-gun to provide its heaviest firepower. Opportunities to engage the enemy with whole belts of ammo from a GPMG are relatively rare, so the L4 often makes better sense in this situation.

Bren Gun

The Bren Gun was the first British light machine gun, adopted from the Czech ZB vz.27 in the 1930s and intended to replace the outdated Lewis gun. Such are its qualities that it is still in service today with the British Army, though designated the L4A4 LMG and changed from .303-in to 7.62-mm NATO calibre. The Bren is solid, reliable, comfortable to use and highly accurate and many question whether its replacement – the Enfield Light Support Weapon (LSW) – can beat the Bren's superb abilities.

Today's Bren
The modern L4A4 Light Machine Gun is the most modern version of the Bren. The L4 series was introduced when the 7.62-mm NATO cartridge was standardized in the British Army in the 1950s. Improvements over the original Bren include a chrome-plated barrel interior, this dramatically improving the barrel durability and reducing the need for barrel changes. Because the 7.62-mm round has no rim, the L4 weapons have straight rather than curved magazines.

Firing

Firing the Bren is simple, and the skills of its use easy to impart. The magazine is inserted securely into the magazine housing, then the cocking handle along the side of the receiver is drawn back, this chambering the first round. Above the trigger is the selector lever which can be placed in either safe, single-shot, or full-automatic positions. Select a fire position and pull the trigger.

Barrel change

The Bren gun barrel can be changed in seconds by releasing the barrel catch and sliding it off the body of the weapon using the carrying handle. Barrel changes are required about every 200–300 rounds depending on the rapidity of fire, though even when the barrel is actually glowing red the gun will maintain an impressive accuracy. The carrying handle is wooden so that it does not conduct barrel heat and burn the operator's hand.

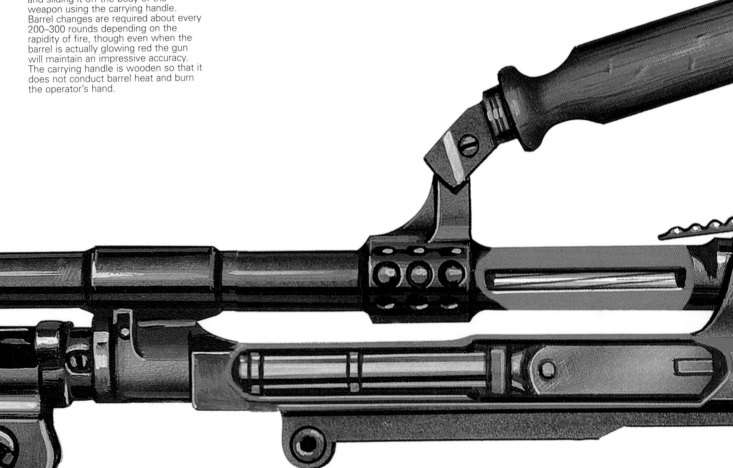

Gas operated

The Bren is a gas-operated weapon. The gas regulator is situated under the barrel and is used to adjust the amount of gas used to force the gas piston back and operate the weapon. This regulator has four different settings. Typically, the Bren fires at about 500rpm; slow compared to other machine guns (the LSW fires at 700–800rpm) but a factor which contributes to its accuracy.

Machine-guns & stormtroopers

Light machine-guns were one of the key weapons to emerge from World War I. While the heavy, water-cooled machine-guns were a major cause of trench warfare — making dug-in troops very difficult to defeat — light machine-guns helped to restore mobility. It should not be forgotten that the greatest breakthrough on the Western Front did not involve tanks. When the Germans defeated the British 5th Army in 1918, they relied on a combination of infantry assault teams, light machine-guns and man-portable mortars. Both sides came to rely on their LMGs both for keeping the defenders' heads down during an attack and for holding a recently captured position before heavier weapons could be brought forward.

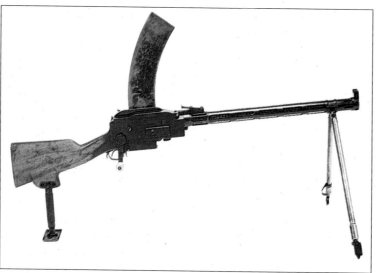

Above: Light machine-guns were so important to the new German tactics that they used lightened versions of their Maxim guns. But these still weighed over 20 kg, and were no substitute for the real thing.

Left: The Danish Madsen was the first light machine-gun to be produced in quantity. Danish citizens even bought them privately as part of a patriotic effort during World War I. They were supplied to both sides during the war and were used by the Germans in their great offensive of 1918.

German soldiers practise their new assault tactics during the winter of 1917. Covered by light machine-gun teams, their riflemen advanced by rushes to lob grenades into the British trenches. Note how they go forward with their rifles slung, stick grenades at the ready.

Below and inset: The British 5.56-mm Light Support Weapon is fitted with the SUSAT x4 sight, which is a great aid to accurate shooting. The sight is protected by a robust mounting, although there have been problems with it misting up during jungle warfare training in Belize.

Telescopic sights

Several modern light machine-guns are fitted with telescopic sights that improve their accuracy at longer ranges and in poor light conditions. The British LSW has the same SUSAT sight as the 5.56-mm SA80 rifle it was developed from. This has ×4 magnification and helps the LSW perform well at over 600 metres — no mean feat given the limitations of 5.56-mm ammunition. When the light is weak, for example on a drizzly winter's afternoon, it is difficult to shoot accurately with standard iron sights. They merge with the gloom and soldiers can find themselves shooting well off target if they are not careful. By magnifying the image, telescopic sights can produce a big improvement in this situation.

Sighting

The earliest Bren guns (Mk 1) had the range set on a drum which extended from 200 to 1800yds. This aperture and post system was rather complex, and by the Mk 3 Bren (pictured here), simple leaf sights were in use. Because of the tall top-mounted magazine, the front sight is offset to the left to allow the operator a clear sight picture.

Firing mechanism

When the Bren's trigger is pulled, a hammer is released which impacts on the back of a firing pin. The firing pin is in turn driven forward onto the primer of the chambered round – it will not make contact if the round is not properly seated – this detonating the cartridge and firing the bullet. Recoil is controlled by a powerful recoil spring in the butt, and the Bren is totally controllable even during sustained fire.

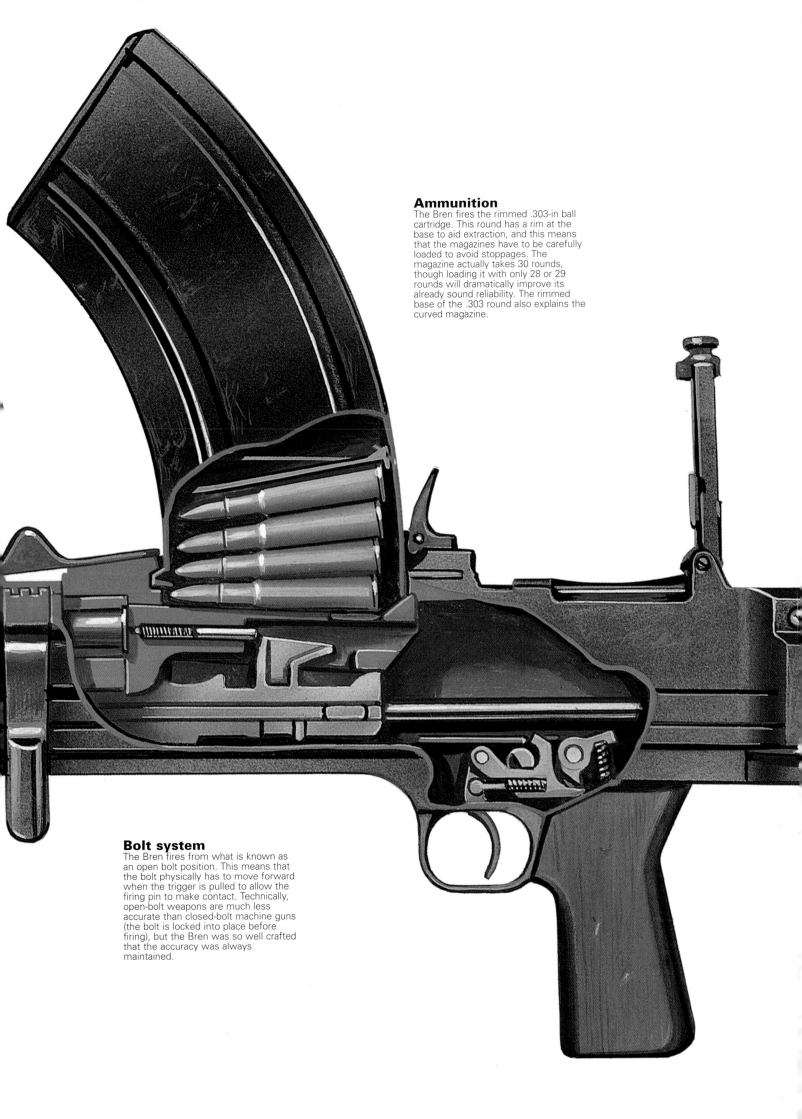

Ammunition
The Bren fires the rimmed .303-in ball cartridge. This round has a rim at the base to aid extraction, and this means that the magazines have to be carefully loaded to avoid stoppages. The magazine actually takes 30 rounds, though loading it with only 28 or 29 rounds will dramatically improve its already sound reliability. The rimmed base of the .303 round also explains the curved magazine.

Bolt system
The Bren fires from what is known as an open bolt position. This means that the bolt physically has to move forward when the trigger is pulled to allow the firing pin to make contact. Technically, open-bolt weapons are much less accurate than closed-bolt machine guns (the bolt is locked into place before firing), but the Bren was so well crafted that the accuracy was always maintained.

Magazines

Many 5.56-mm light machine-guns take advantage of the relatively small size of their ammunition and use very large-capacity magazines. Whereas the British LSW conservatively uses standard 30-round magazines as used by the SA80 rifle, the Belgian Minimi adopted by the US Army uses a large plastic box carrying 200 rounds. The Ultimax uses 100-round drum magazines and the Spanish Ameli also crams 200 rounds into its plastic magazines.

How light is a light machine-gun?

The FN MAG 7.62-mm General Purpose Machine Gun weighs 10.85 kg with no ammunition loaded. By comparison, the British LSW and the Belgian Minimi both weigh 6.88 kg with no ammunition. The Spanish Ameli is similar and only weighs 9.3 kg with a 200-round magazine attached. Combat experience in the Falklands showed just how rapidly troops can use up their ammunition. As a result, any weight-saving that will allow soldiers to carry more bullets is well worthwhile.

Above: The Belgian Minimi, adopted by the US Army as the M249 Squad Automatic Weapon (SAW), is shown here with the 5.56-mm FNC folding stock assault rifle. Their similar appearance makes it harder for enemy troops to single out the machine-gunner.

Above, right and below: The Ultimax 100 can be fired from the hip like a Chicago gangster's Thompson gun. Even better, you do not have to be built like Sylvester Stallone to manage it, and the 5.56-mm ammunition it fires does not produce much recoil.

Assault tactics

John Rambo may be able to swing a 7.62-mm M60 General Purpose Machine Gun from his hip, but in reality it is very difficult to hit anything. Unless the target is in the same room, hitting it with a 7.62-mm machine-gun is a major challenge. The new range of light machine-guns chambered for the 5.56-mm cartridge are far more suitable. LMGs like the Ultimax or Ameli weigh little more than an assault rifle and, since their ammunition weighs only half as much as an equivalent quantity of 7.62-mm, they can carry more or travel very light indeed.

BATTLING in the bush

In Rhodesia, the security forces depended on training and firepower to defeat the guerrillas. A former soldier in the Rhodesian army describes a battle.

One incident that is engraved on my memory now seems comical, but at the time it was bloody frightening. In the heat of battle, I discovered I'd left half my Bren gun behind!

It happened when I was a member of a four-man stick on a riverline patrol. Our stick, Two One Charlie, was sweeping the western bank of the small, dried-out Togwe river, while another stick – Two One Delta – swept the other bank. We were searching for signs of communist guerrillas (codenamed Charlie Tango) which Special Branch had told us were using the riverline to infiltrate the urban and industrial midlands provinces of Rhodesia.

We were told to keep a lookout for any possible camps and sleeping places and, of course, the CTs themselves. It seemed it was going to be just another routine patrol for us 19- and 20-year-olds, most of us hardened veterans of

Above: A soldier opens fire with the British L4 Bren gun mounted on a tripod. The box magazine restricts the L4's ability to provide sustained fire, but it does have the facility for a quick barrel change.

scores of encounters with Charlie Tango.

We were dropped off on the move about an hour before dawn – a tactic designed to prevent the locals hearing our vehicles stop and alerting every CT within a 50-km radius. It was pitch black, so we kept close to each other in single file.

After walking for about 15 minutes the silence was shattered by the sound of heavy steel smashing into rocks, a thud and then something crashing into the dry, brittle bush. A hushed voice from the other side of the river said, "Fuck! I'm sorry!" We remained motionless, and Paddy, the corporal leading Two One

parallel to the river. If there was anything to be found, we would find it.

By keeping regular radio contact and with occasional visual sightings, the two sticks progressed at the same rate so that if either stick walked into something too hot to handle, the other stick would be in a position to execute a flanking attack. At least, that was the theory.

Meandering river

As it happened, the riverbed started to meander into wild, erratic bends and curves. The bush itself started to turn against us, especially in my path, where thorns tore at my arms, legs and face. We had radio contact with Two One Delta but hadn't been able to see them for more than an hour. It wasn't yet eight o'clock, but already my shirt was saturated. Sweat was trickling into my eyes and stinging like blazes, and thousands of bloody flies were drinking the sweat on the back of my shirt, up my nostrils, in my mouth and in my ears. They were the second enemy.

I saw Corporal Cummings raise his right hand and I stopped, slipping my Bren gun strap from my shoulder in one instinctive movement. He was examining something on the ground: an empty Chinese cigarette pack.

Below: This soldier from the Rhodesian SAS is armed with a Soviet RPD 7.62-mm light machine-gun captured from the guerrillas. Note the sack under the gun, which contains a belt of ammunition. The Soviet drum magazines tended to rattle.

Above: A group photograph of Rhodesian SAS on a long-range recce patrol. Deliberately emulating their opponents, they wear Portuguese camouflage jackets and are armed with Soviet weapons. All but one carry RPD light machine-guns rather than a rifle.

Delta, whispered on the blower that his gunner had fallen into an aardvark hole.

As dawn broke we spread out, keeping about eight metres between each man. Then our stick leader, Corporal Cummings, without saying a word, held his arms out at his sides and we immediately changed from single file into an extended line. So there we were, two sticks patrolling, one each side of a riverbed, about 10 metres between each man, following his own imaginary line

A concealed observation post is manned with an FN FAL heavy barrel rifle – a cross between an assault rifle and a light machine-gun, also used by Argentina in the Falklands campaign.

BATTLING IN THE BUSH

Hardly likely to have arrived there under normal circumstances in the sanctions-plagued Rhodesian bush.

We seemed to have found a place where about 30 people had slept and probably moved out only hours previously. We would have missed it but for that carelessly-discarded cigarette pack. The rest of the stick went on to unearth dozens of empty food tins, all of them of Communist origin, and some ammo.

Corporal Cummings briefed Two One Delta and warned them to be double 'switched on'. Neither of us knew whether we were in front of or behind the other stick, but we had to carry on and hope that fate would bring us together again. None of us was feeling easy. We thought of ourselves as better soldiers than Charlie Tango, but those odds of 30 against eight would have sent any bookie running.

The sun was really starting to scorch us now. The bush was as evil as ever, ripping and clawing at us, and the soil was now soft, sandy and unbearable to walk on. Then a virtually open area came up in front, with only the odd bit of knee-high regrowth. We reached the edge of this 'oasis' and I remember saying to myself, "Thank Christ for that." It was about 60 metres across – 60 metres of heaven before being ripped by thorns again.

We automatically increased the distance between ourselves to suit this different type of terrain. Then, about halfway across, I thought I saw a movement in the bushline ahead of us. That was my last rational thought for some time: from that moment, instinct took over.

There was one solitary crack of rifle fire, followed by a roar and then an explosion of automatic fire. The entire bushline ahead of us seemed to erupt, spewing thick white smoke in a line about 100 metres across. We had walked blindly into one hell of an ambush.

Below: An L4 Bren gun covers a river crossing. The long range of a light machine-gun is particularly useful for covering such open areas, particularly against an enemy without air support or many heavy weapons.

Left: The dramatic slash pattern of Rhodesian camouflage worked well in the bush, where the vegetation often cast dark shadows over the light earth and scrub. Note how even the FN FAL rifle has been daubed with paint to produce a mottled effect.

After hearing the first shot I fired roughly into the ambush area ahead of me, managed another step forward and dived to the ground, still firing. I pulled down the bipod legs of my Bren and started putting short bursts into likely cover. The grass and sand around was exploding as enemy firepower began homing in. I caught a glimpse of my forearms as I changed magazines and panic surged through me as I saw them covered with a gory mess of blood and dirt.

They were firing 60-mm mortars at us now, which hopelessly overshot and sent deadly wooden shrapnel into the air as trees disintegrated. Rocket-propelled grenades were exploding to our rear, much closer than the mortars. RPG blast carries forward; if Charlie Tango had aimed the rockets to detonate to our front, things would have been disastrous.

Head for the high ground

A bit of a lull in the firing gave Corporal Cummings enough time to assess our predicament. He yelled at me to get to a slight rise about 12 paces away – although it looked like 1,200 paces! Adrenalin was doing its job. What the hell! I slid to the side of my Bren, grabbed at the carrying handle and made a crazed dash for the high ground, drawing increased enemy fire.

I had taken half a dozen paces before I realised something was terribly wrong. The gun! I didn't have my Bren with me! At least, I didn't have all of it: I was holding the carrying handle and the barrel, but by some horrific trick of fate I must have unclipped the barrel-detaching lever. It was no bloody good to me like that, so I dived back to my original firing position and hastily reconnected the barrel to the gun, burning my hands quite badly in the process. I repeated my dash, took up position and opened fire.

I glanced to my left and saw Corporal Cummings and the other guys pick themselves up and start

Carefully lifting off from a bush landing zone, an Alouette helicopter heads for home. As the war intensified, heliborne assaults were used to insert blocking forces against guerrilla bands intercepted by the security forces.

running towards the ambush position. I followed suit, firing all the time. Charlie Tango began running in all directions, many of them firing over their shoulders. We ran through their position and carried on for another 50 metres before Corporal Cummings shouted for us to re-organise ourselves around him, and he radioed Two One Delta.

Almost at once we could hear them nearby, firing at remnants of Charlie Tango who had unwittingly run right into them. Within minutes we saw Two One Delta – a bit late, but very welcome all the same. We combined the two sticks and

swept back through the area we had just assaulted. Seven Charlie Tango lay dead; another two were alive but seriously wounded. We retrieved a large quantity of weapons, ammunition, food and medical supplies.

Miraculously, casualties on our side were negligible. I was about the worst, with my burned hands; the unsightly mess on my arms was nothing worse than the results of sand-blasting. Ironically, the soft, sandy soil that I had cursed earlier had saved my life – if the ground had been hard, I would have been ripped to pieces by ricochets.

Special Branch arrived later in

Above: The Rhodesian's air support was limited but effective. This Alouette helicopter mounts a 20-mm cannon, which could bring down accurate fire on guerrilla concentrations.

the day to pick up the wounded Charlie Tangos and the vast amount of equipment abandoned by the rest of the gang. They also carried out a detailed inspection of the ambush site, collecting expended cartridges and shells for forensic tests. They told us we had been mistaken in our estimated figure of 30 enemy: we had in fact carried out an assault on about 100 Charlie Tangos.

FIRE AND MANOEUVRE

When the British Army introduced the Light Support Weapon, it replaced a high-firing, hard-hitting GPMG firing 7.62-mm rounds with a lightweight machine-gun firing fewer, and smaller, rounds. Why?

Before the introduction of the LSW, the typical British squad was made up of eight men: section commander, section 2IC, GPMG gunner and his number two, and four riflemen. The squad would work in two teams. The first, the gun group, was made up of the section 2IC, and the GPMG gunner and number two on the gun. The second team was made up of the four riflemen, commanded by the section leader. The gun group would put down suppressive fire on the position while the rifle team would skirt round to a flank and assault the position from there. That was the theory.

Like most theories, there is a yawning gap between the niceties of planning and the reality of hot lead flying around you. Experiences in the Falklands quickly established that the old gun group-rifle team formation was simply not working. What was needed was a radical appraisal of squad tactics and the weapons to go with them.

The result of this was the introduction of the LSW. Instead of one medium machine-gun per squad, there would be two light ones. This meant that, at a stroke, the flexibility of

the squad was drastically increased. It was now possible to arrange the squad in a number of ways, balanced according to the situation.

The other result learned from the Falklands was that, whereas beforehand it was rather optimistically thought that to clear a platoon-size enemy position would take a company something in the order of 30-40 minutes, the reality was something much more like six to seven hours, and the consumption of ammo was way off the scale. The logic of having a common ammo with your machine-gun becomes even more apparent (the GPMG is 7.62-mm; the SA80 and LSW are both 5.56-mm).

With the replacement of the SLR by the SA80, the organisation of the platoon is now:

section commander	SA80
rifleman	SA80
rifleman	SA80
LSW gunner	LSW
LSW gunner	LSW
section 2IC	SA80
rifleman	SA80
rifleman	SA80

Paras patrol the borders of South Armagh equipped with SA80 and the LSW. The increased accuracy of these weapons over the old SLR rifle and the LMG led to a shift in IRA tactics away from sniping and ambushes towards command-detonated mines: the terrorists realized that there was too great a chance of coming second in a fire fight.

Above and below: The main advantage of the new LSW is its accuracy. The SUSAT sight and long barrel enable a skilled gunner to place a hit on a man at 800 metres with relative ease. To the enemy the gunner is difficult to distinguish from the other members of the section except at very close range: this means he is more likely to survive in a firefight.

Right: A gunner changes mags on his LSW. The weapon lacks sustained firepower as a 30-round magazine does not go far in the average fire fight.

1 Two-fireteam section

The squad will divide into two equal fireteams of three SA80s and one LSW. One fireteam will be commanded by the section commander, the other by the section 2IC. They can operate together or as two independent teams. This will be the usual way of splitting up the squad in the advance. The advantage is that the teams are equally balanced to respond and can provide an equal support to each other.

2 Manoeuvre team and support team

The support team is composed of the two LSWs under the command of the section 2IC plus one rifleman. The manoeuvre team is led by the section commander and has three other riflemen in it. In this case the teams are pre-planned, with the support team acting something like the old gun group would have done. This allows a concentration of force but at the expense of flexibility. If the support team is contacted first it may have to be extracted before it can carry out its role. The manoeuvre team lacks the firepower to support them in an assault.

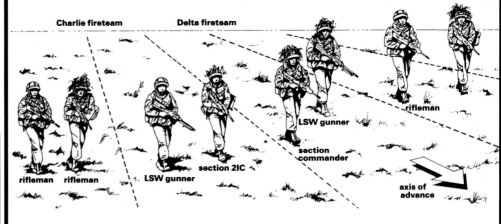

Charlie fireteam   Delta fireteam

rifleman

LSW gunner

section commander

rifleman   rifleman   LSW gunner   section 2IC

axis of advance

3 Pairs

The two fireteams can be broken down even further. By dividing the teams in half you get four pairs; two with LSWs, two without. This is the usual formation for the assault once the squad has come under effective enemy fire. By breaking down into pairs it means that one man can move forward while the other puts down suppressive fire. Once the moving man has gone no more than five paces, he will drop and put down covering fire for his partner. This way the squad can advance while keeping up a hail of fire. The LSW teams will operate so that LSW fire is maintained, i.e. both gunners will not be down at the same time.

Increased accuracy means that less ammunition is wasted and supporting fire in the assault can be brought down a few feet in front of the assaulting troops with relative safety, enabling the troops to get right on top of the enemy trench before the gunner has to switch fire. The advantages of both rifle and LSW taking the same ammo in the same magazine cannot be understated: a rifleman can just throw a gunner extra mags. Prior to SA80, this was only possible in sections equipped with SLRs and 7.62-mm L4 Bren guns.

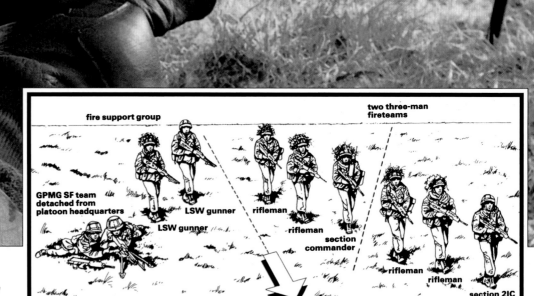

fire support group

two three-man fireteams

GPMG SF team detached from platoon headquarters

LSW gunner   rifleman

LSW gunner

rifleman

section commander

rifleman

rifleman

section 2IC

4 Gun group/rifle group

While fighting in a built-up area or during counter-revolutionary warfare or other low intensity operations, there may be a place for the old gun group/rifle group. In this case a GPMG(SF) (a conventional GPMG with a heavy barrel designed for heavy firepower — SF stands for Sustained Fire) will be attached to the squad from the battalion's support weapons company (a grouping of all the medium support weapons, e.g. GPMG(SF), 81-mm mortars, MILAN etc). In this case the LSW gunners will attach themselves to the gun group to provide extra fire. The remaining six men from the squad will form two three-man fireteams and will fire-and-manoeuvre by fireteam.

SNIPER RIFLE

The body lay where it fell, halfway between two British trenches. It would have to stay there until after dark: movement in daylight was now impossible. Hostile eyes patiently watched the whole area, prepared to wait for hour after hour for someone else to make a mistake. All work on the defences was paralysed. But some of the shootings aroused suspicion: several men had been shot in the back. A few soldiers slipped back towards the rear to make a search.

"While they were halted beside a large strawrick one of the men noticed some empty German cartridge cases at his feet. On thrusting their bayonets into the rick the party was rewarded by a yell and a German coming out headlong. Inside was a comfortable hide, having openings cleverly blocked with straw, and a week's supply of food. The sniper could come out at night for exercise and water. Only his carelessness with his used cartridges cost

him his life, for his was finished there and then."

This particular sniper died in October 1914 at the hands of the 2nd Royal Welch. But the ability of one well-trained rifleman to pin down large bodies of troops was demonstrated in both World Wars, Vietnam and the Falklands. Sniping is a job for loners, and there is far more to it than simply being a good shot. Lying up behind the enemy lines like this demands incredible patience and self-confidence. The ability to move without being seen or to remain in a cramped, cold, hiding place for days on end is essential. An American sniper in Vietnam spent a whole day crawling the last few hundred metres to reach his firing position. Having shot dead a Vietnamese officer, he then took another full day to crawl away unseen.

If all this effort is to be rewarded, the sniper must have an accurate rifle. Modern armies

Modern sniper rifles have proved their value in most 20th and 21st century conflicts. A well-trained sniper with a good rifle is the most dangerous man on the battlefield.

Below: Equipped with a rifle that far out-ranges those of ordinary riflemen, the sniper can pick off his targets while remaining unseen. This Yugoslavian sniper is aiming an M76. Note his mesh facemask and camouflage mittens.

The SAS uses .50-calibre sniper rifles to destroy unexploded bombs from 1000 metres away.

equip their snipers with purpose-built weapons to give their snipers the best chance of a first-round kill at 800 metres or more. Accurate shooting is achieved by ironing out as many inconsistencies as possible. The trigger action must be exceptionally smooth so that every shot is squeezed off in the same way. The ammunition must be manufactured with great care to ensure that every round behaves in exactly the same way. The performance of standard factory-made ammunition always varies slightly; so most snipers use special 'match grade' ammunition produced with much greater quality control. Others, like the British SAS, have their ammunition hand-loaded for maximum consistency.

Telescopic sights

The sights are equally important, and their price can match that of the rifle itself. Top-quality telescopic sights now cost over £1,000 each. Heavy barrels are another important factor in a sniper rifle's accuracy, but they create obvious problems for the soldier. Creeping across hostile country is tiring

Above: This British Royal Marine sniper is armed with the 7.62-mm L96 sniper rifle. Built by hand from a target shooting design, this weapon has proved a sturdy and accurate addition to British Army sniping.

enough without a rifle weighing 8-10kg!

The value of specially trained soldiers, able to pick off enemy officers, was recognised as early as the English Civil War. But it was not until the 18th century that British and American gunmakers provided rifles sufficiently accurate to make this possible. The modern British Army's Light Division consists of regiments which included the first true battlefield snipers. In the Peninsula war, French officers bravely led their men from the front where they were shot down with Baker rifles. The brutal efficiency of British riflemen was widely known. At Waterloo, the incompetent Prince of Orange, commanding British troops thanks to his political connections, was fortunately shot and replaced. It was widely rumoured that the Duke of Wellington had despatched a British rifleman to do the deed!

Another famous victim of a battlefield sniper was the American General Sedgwick, commander of the Union V Corps during the American civil war. Chiding his men for taking cover hundreds of yards from the enemy, he shouted, "Don't worry, men, they couldn't hit an elephant at this distance." Seconds later,

Red Army Snipers

In the modern Soviet army, every platoon includes a sniper with a specially-designed rifle. The Soviets' enthusiasm for sniping dates back to World War II, when the Red Army's snipers inflicted a constant stream of losses on the German forces.

The Russian snipers' usual weapon was the Mosin-Nagant 7.62-mm rifle fitted with a ×3.5 telescopic sight. The scope mounting could be removed easily so that the sniper could quickly hide the evidence of his or her trade: both sides tended to execute captured snipers. Some of the most successful Russian snipers were women, and the best shots accounted for over 200 enemy soldiers each.

Above left: A Soviet sniper takes aim with an SVT-40 self-loading sniper rifle.

Left: One of the Red Army's formidable women snipers.

SNIPER RIFLE Reference File

63 UNITED KINGDOM

L42A1 7.62-mm rifle

This is a modified version of the famous Lee-Enfield bolt action rifle used by British infantrymen since 1895. British snipers used standard service weapons until 1942, when modified No. 4 rifles were introduced. Designated No. 4 Mk 1 (T), they were fitted with cheek pieces and a mount for a telescopic sight. They served until the 1950s when they were replaced by a new version, the L42. This has been used by British Army and Royal Marine snipers ever since. It was developed from a target-shooting version of the Lee-Enfield produced in 7.62-mm calibre when the British Army adopted the SLR. The L42 has a special heavyweight barrel and several modifications to the trigger and

magazine, and is fitted with iron sights and attachments for a telescopic sight or image intensifier. The wooden fore-end is that of the No. 4 .303-in rifle, but dramatically cut down; and the stock is taken straight from a No. 4. Although highly successful from Aden to the Falklands, advances in rifle designs make it distinctly old-fashioned. Unfortunately, when the Army selected a In 1986 a new rifle was adopted as the British Army standard – the Accuracy International L86A1. This is actually a development of a civilian competition rifle, and though it had several years of teething troubles it is now an established and proven weapon. However, the solidity of the L42A1 means that they still appear in action.

Specification
Cartridge: 7.62-mm×51
Operation: manual
Feed: 10-round magazine
Weight: 4.43kg
Overall length: 1181mm
Barrel length: 699mm

British snipers have used the L42 since the 1950s. Chambered for 7.62-mm NATO, it is the latest service version of the Lee-Enfield rifle introduced in the 1890s. The British Army still prefers a bolt action rifle for sniping, rejecting self-loading weapons.

a Confederate sharpshooter put a bullet through his head.

Modern snipers are expected to be able to hit a man at 800 metres. Shooting at this sort of range has been possible since the bolt-action metal cartridge rifles of the 1890s were introduced. The current British sniper rifle, the L42, is simply a modified Lee-Enfield that any soldier of World War I would instantly recognise. There are few recorded instances of accurate sniping at much longer ranges, although German snipers in Normandy fired on British airstrips from well over a kilometre. A buffalo hunter in the group attacked by Comanche and Cheyenne Indians in 1874 achieved the best shot in American history by picking one man off his horse at a distance (later paced out) of over 1200 metres.

Massive bullets

Only one modern rifle offers the sniper a longer reach than his counterparts of World War I. Several American manufacturers have developed rifles firing .50-cal (12.7-mm calibre) bullets. Barrett produces a monstrous semi-automatic sniper rifle; McMillan

Above: A Royal Marine sniper is seen in action in Aden during 1967. His Enfield rifle is little different to those used by British troops in World War I. Highly accurate and thoroughly reliable, the ultimate version of the SMLE will probably still be in service 100 years after the first ones were issued.

Right: Two American snipers demonstrate typically outlandish camouflage suits, which all snipers use to merge with the background. It is vital to break up the distinctive human outline and the shape of the rifle.

has already sold 50 of their bolt-action .50-cal to the Turkish army. This massive bullet can only be fired from an equally substantial weapon, and the 10-kg bulk of these weapons makes shooting from any position other than prone very difficult. With a suitable scope and favourable opportunity, a McMillan is effective to over 2000 metres. Armour-piercing ammunition enables it to deal with light armoured vehicles too.

64

SVD Dragunov

Former USSR

Every Soviet rifle platoon has a sniper armed with the SVD sniper rifle. The AK-74 rifles and light machine-guns of the rest of the unit are only effective at up to 500 metres at most. The average conscript is not a particularly good shot, but the Soviet army has always recognised the value of a sniper for killing enemy officers and weapons crew. Like all Soviet small arms, the SVD is light, well balanced and simple to operate. It fires the old 7.62-mm×54 rimmed cartridge, introduced in the 1890s and still used by the Soviet PK general-purpose machine-gun. The PSO-1 4×24 telescopic sight incorporates a simple scale based on the height of a man. This gives a good indication of the range and helps the

SVD achieve single-shot kills at 800 metres. Although the SVD uses the same basic bolt system as the AK series assault rifles, it has had to be modified. The long stroke gas piston in an AK creates unacceptable movement in a weapon intended for precise accuracy. So a lightweight piston is substituted in the Dragunov, transferring its energy to the bolt head. This short-stroke mechanism prevents any major change in the rifle's centre of gravity during firing. The SVD has been supplied to most members of the Warsaw Pact, and was most recently seen in action during the Romanian revolution in December 1989.

Specification
Cartridge: 7.62-mm×54R
Operation: gas
Feed: 10-round detachable box
Weight: 4.3 kg with scope
Overall length: 1225 mm
Barrel length: 622 mm

The SVD Dragunov is a self-loading rifle that eliminates the need for the sniper to move to chamber the next round. This is theoretically less accurate, but the practical difference is counterbalanced by the greater security afforded to the sniper.

The Essentials of a Sniper Rifle

Adjustable trigger
The trigger pull should not only be smooth and easy; for best results, it should be adjustable so that the individual shooter can tailor it to suit himself.

Telescopic sight
At 1000 metres or more, a man-sized target appears no bigger than a pin. A powerful scope is essential for accurate long-range shooting.

Match grade barrel
A purpose-built barrel produced with much greater quality control than a standard military rifle produces much greater consistency.

Bipod
Rifles like this McMillan ELR .50-calibre are best fired from a bipod for maximum stability. Resting the barrel on something else can cause major loss of accuracy.

Side arm
Sniper rifles are too cumbersome for use at close quarters. For emergencies, a sniper should carry a pistol, in this case a CZ75 9-mm.

Recoil pad
Adjustable to suit the individual firer, this is essential on a .50-cal and important on a 7.62-mm rifle.

Special purpose ammunition
These rounds are armour-piercing incendiary, used for knocking out light armoured vehicles. For shooting enemy troops, match grade ammunition is essential. Ordinary factory-made rounds are not consistent enough for maximum accuracy.

65

YUGOSLAVIA

M76 sniper rifle

Yugoslavia is one of the many countries to manufacture its own versions of Soviet weapons. They have produced a carbine, closely based on the SKS, and a pair of assault rifles very similar to the AKM. Like the Soviet SVD Dragunov, the M76 uses the same basic system of operation as the Kalashnikov rifles. Apart from the longer barrel and smaller, straighter magazine, the M76 looks almost identical to a Yugoslavian-built AK. It is available in several different calibres, including 7.62-mm NATO and the German 7.92-mm cartridge used during both world wars. This is still used by some Yugoslavian machine-guns, so it is not as peculiar a choice as it may appear. The M76 has a ×4 sight, closely modelled on the PSO-1

on the SVD. It has a sweeping range of 320 metres for a head silhouette and up to 620 metres for a running target. Maximum effective range is 800 metres and the scope mounting is also designed to fit a night vision device.

Specification
Cartridge: 7.62-mm or 7.92-mm
Operation: gas
Feed: 10-round detachable box magazine
Weight: 4.2 kg
Overall length: 1135 mm
Barrel length: 550 mm

The M76 bears a striking likeness to the Soviet SVD. It is available in two calibres: the choice of 7.62-mm NATO was obviously made with an eye on the export market.

66

WEST GERMANY

Heckler & Koch PSG-1
Präzisionsschützengewehr

The current West German army sniper rifle, the PSG-1 (precision-shooting rifle) is a true heavyweight. Solidly constructed with a very thick and heavy barrel, the cheek-piece and the angle of the butt can be adjusted to suit the individual firer. The 6×42 telescopic sight has an illuminated reticle to help shooting in poor light conditions. The PSG-1 is undeniably accurate, but it is perhaps better suited to police actions rather than military use. Weighing almost twice as much as the Soviet SVD, it is not the best weapon to have to crawl about the country with.

Like the Soviets, the Germans have been quite happy with a semi-

automatic weapon rather than a bolt-action. The PSG-1 uses the famous Heckler & Koch roller locking system encountered on the G3 rifle and MP5 sub-machine gun. Firing .308 Lapua match grade ammunition at 200 metres, the PSG-1 can produce 10-round groups 8 cm across.

Specification
Cartridge: 7.62-mm NATO
Operation: delayed blowback
Feed: 5- or 20-round detachable magazine
Weight: 8.1 kg
Overall length: 1208 mm
Barrel length: 650 mm

The Heckler & Koch PSG-1 is one of the heaviest standard 7.62-mm sniper rifles in military service. It is a fine and accurate weapon, but its size is uncomfortably close to the .50-calibre monsters now available from several American rifle manufacturers.

The concentration on range is only worthwhile in certain circumstances. Although there were some spectacular long-range shoots in Vietnam, the typical sniper engagement was very different. In a sample of sniper kills achieved by men of the 6/31st Infantry during one month, the average engagement range was 148 metres. The US snipers killed 39 Viet Cong, all during night ambushes using hunting rifles or service M14s with night sights. Most engagements took place between midnight and 1 a.m. The Viet Cong and North Vietnamese also made extensive use of snipers, concentrating on American officers, machine-gunners, radio operators and medics. Like the Soviet army in World War II, some of their snipers were women. Most relied on standard military rifles with telescopic sights; few had purpose-built weapons.

Soviet sniper rifles

The Soviet army was one of the first to introduce specially designed sniper rifles. In the early 1960s they replaced their World War I vintage Mosin-Nagant rifles with the SVD Dragunov. Chambered for the same 1890s cartridge, it is a semi-automatic rifle with a scope providing ×4 magnification. Soviet snipers are usually selected from those con-

British snipers wear purpose-made sniper jackets that have padded elbows to make long crawls slightly less uncomfortable. Strips of hessian disguise his shape and prevent the sun glinting off his rifle.

67
FRANCE

Fusil à Répétition Modèle F1 (FR-F1)

This is the French equivalent to the British L42: a sniper rifle developed from an obsolete bolt-action weapon after World War II. In this case the rifle was the Model 1936 version that fired the French 7.5-mm cartridge. The FR-F1 appeared in time for the French army's long and bitter campaign in Algeria. Fitted with the M1953 scope, it provided French units with an effective long-range weapon at a time when many formations relied mainly on MAT-49 sub-machine guns. It has continued to serve wherever French forces have intervened in Africa. The French army follows the Soviet practice in attaching one sniper to each infantry platoon's headquarters. Some have now been produced chambered for

7.62-mm NATO as France finally abandoned its 7.5-mm cartridge.

Specification
Cartridge: 7.5-mm×54 or 7.62-mm×51
Operation: manual
Feed: 10-round magazine
Weight: 5.2 kg
Overall length: 1138 mm
Barrel length: 552 mm

Like the Soviets, the French attach a sniper to each rifle platoon. The FR-F1 is their standard sniping rifle. Used on battlefields from the Algerian war to Beirut and Chad, it has proved highly successful.

68
UNITED KINGDOM

Parker Hale M85

This is about as accurate a rifle as it is possible to build. Used as a civilian target rifle, it has proved exceptionally accurate and has been adopted by various armies and police units worldwide. Its distinctive American-made plastic stocks come in black, green, or disruptive patterned finishes including desert, arctic, forest and urban camouflage. The superb accuracy of the free-floating heavy barrel is guaranteed for 5,000 rounds and the rifle can be fitted with a variety of scopes. As a rule of thumb, it is worth spending almost as much on the scope as on the rifle. This will give maximum accuracy. The M85 has a silently operated safety catch so that the sniper will not be betrayed by the loud click

produced by some weapons including the SVD sniper rifle. The butt is covered by a rubber recoil pad and the pistol grip has a rough surface to make it non-slip. An M85, costing around £1,000, fitted with an appropriate scope, will put all five rounds into a 50p piece at 600 metres.

Specification
Cartridge: 7.62-mm×51
Operation: manual
Feed: 10-round box
Weight: 13-14 kg depending on scope
Overall length: 1150 mm
Barrel length: 700 mm

The Parker Hale M85 is an outstanding sniper rifle seen here in the 'woodland' and 'urban' pattern camouflage stocks. Note the Samson 7.62-mm cartridges, favoured by many snipers, and the hoods on the scopes that keep light off the lens.

A British sniper uses a scoped Lee-Enfield from the roof of a shattered house during street fighting in Germany, 1945. German snipers would be one of his prime targets as they regularly held up the Allied advance.

scripts who proved themselves good shots in DOSAAF, the communist party youth organisation. Marksmanship has been encouraged in the USSR since the 1930s, when factories and offices were all part of the workers' mil-

A platoon sniper of the 2nd French Foreign Legion Paratroop regiment is armed with an FR-F1 sniper rifle. This has a bipod fitted to provide greater stability: resting a rifle barrel on something can cause major loss of accuracy.

itia, trained to defend their country.

Specially-designed sniper rifles can be very expensive. Whereas the SVD is a straight-forward and relatively inexpensive weapon, the latest sniper rifles cost several thousand pounds each. There is certainly a law of diminishing returns – spending twice as much on a rifle will not necessarily make it twice as accurate – but it is not a large sum of money when compared to the cost of training top snipers. With the right man at the trigger, a modern sniper rifle can put all its rounds through a target the size of a matchbox at 600 metres. But work continues on every aspect of rifle shooting, extending the effective range and the lethality of the ammunition still further.

Combat Comparison

1800 Baker rifle

This was the first rifle to see widespread service with the British Army. Used by light infantry regiments in the Peninsula war and at Waterloo, it was far more accurate than contemporary muskets. British riflemen picked off enemy officers and gunners from hitherto unheard-of distances.

1942 SMLE Rifle No. 4 Mk 1(T)

During World War I, British snipers used standard SMLEs, but in 1942 a specialist sniper version of the No. 4 rifle was introduced. Fitted with a scope mount, tangent rearsight and cheek rest, it was used until the 1950s.

1981 Walther WA2000

Chambered for the Winchester .300 Magnum round, the WA2000 is a purpose-built sniper weapon. The overall length is reduced by a bullpup configuration (placing the trigger group forward of the magazine), which gives it a radically different profile.

1985 Beretta 7.62-mm sniper rifle

Unlike the No. 4 above, this is not a modified version of an existing service rifle. Designed from the beginning for the sniper role, it features a heavy free-floating barrel and is normally fitted with a Zeiss variable-magnification sight.

Sniper rifles first appeared over 450 years ago: Leonardo da Vinci used one of his own design to shoot enemy soldiers besieging Florence. But they only entered regular military service in the late 18th century. Some are modified versions of standard rifles; others are specifically developed for the job. Developments in ammunition and optical sights have pushed effective ranges towards 2000 metres. But the most important factor remains the same: the skill of the rifleman.

Below: The Baker was loaded from the muzzle. This was a problem because accuracy depended on the bullet tightly engaging the rifling in the barrel. The round had to be hammered down, making it much slower to load than standard smoothbore muskets.

Above: Like its contemporaries, the Baker was fired by a flintlock mechanism. The hammer carried a flint that struck sparks into the pan on the side of the action. This ignited a small quantity of black powder and the flash passed through a small hole to fire the main charge behind the bullet.

Above: When British riflemen used the Baker rifle, cavalry were still a major threat. This fearsome sword bayonet turned the Baker into an unwieldy muzzle-heavy weapon, but it was essential in close combat.

Below: Built from a standard service rifle, the No. 4 sniper rifle retained the iron sights of the original. No heavier than the regular weapon, it also kept the bayonet attachment for emergencies.

Above: The Enfield rifle was the first British rifle to use smokeless propellant. Each shot from the Baker produced a large cloud of white smoke that made concealment impossible. Smokeless cartridges were first used to deadly effect in the Boer war.

Above: Standard SMLEs produced five-round groups, 10 cm in diameter at 183 metres (200 yards). The addition of a telescopic sight extended the effective range of the sniper to 1000 metres in favourable conditions.

Below: The WA2000's distinctive profile looks more suited to Olympic shooting competitions than a battlefield. This, and doubts about its reliability in service conditions, have put off some armies from adopting it.

Above: The WA2000 is built around the barrel and the cartridge. Unlike the British SA80 bullpup rifle, the Walther can be switched to allow right- or left-handed operation.

Above: The Beretta reverts to a more conventional appearance. The flash eliminator at the muzzle helps conceal the sniper's position. Another trick is to damp down the ground beneath the muzzle to stop dust being kicked up when the weapon is fired.

Above: The Beretta's bolt action and five-shot magazine are a throwback to earlier 20th century service weapons. But the sniper's demand for accuracy has been given top priority. Rapid fire and high magazine capacity are not strictly necessary.

LONG-RANGED AND
LETHAL: the
.50cal

One sniper in Vietnam recorded confirmed kills at 2500 metres with a scoped .50 M2 heavy machine-gun. This inspired the development of the most powerful weapon that can be carried by a single man, the .50-calibre sniper rifle. This weapon will even destroy armoured vehicles and helicopters.

No sniper likes to get too close to his target. Armed with a long-range precision rifle, it is not his business to get involved in a close-quarter battle. From the sniper's point of view, the greater the effective range of his rifle, the better.

The realistic maximum range of most sniper rifles is a little over 1000 metres. Even the best of the 7.62-mm cartridges, like the Israeli-manufactured Samson match-grade ammunition, would need a lot of luck to hit at much greater distances. And luck is not something a sniper can afford to rely on: his life is at stake.

Several special-purpose rounds have been developed to allow an accurate shot at longer range. The .300 Winchester Magnum is one of several cartridges that have been tested by the military and police 'counter-sniper' teams. But one bullet is the undisputed king of long-range sniping: the .50 calibre.

This 12.7-mm round takes its name from the standard American designation, which is expressed in fractions of an inch. Introduced in 1921, the Browning .50-cal is fired from the M2 heavy machine-gun, which has seen service from World

Left: The incredible destructive power of the .50-cal round is demonstrated by a burst from an M2 Browning. The size of the bullet is sufficient to make armour-piercing incendiary ammunition that will penetrate the armour of APCs and explode inside.

Above: The size of the M2 is obvious from this picture of two South Vietnamese soldiers engaging Viet Cong troops from the back of an M41 Walker Bulldog light tank. Since not even Rambo could carry and shoot an M2, a .50-cal rifle was the obvious solution.

s Today

sniper rifle is another conventional weapon tested by the US Marine Corps as part of its sniper weapons programme. The US Marines revived the art of sniping in the American armed forces during the Vietnam war, and their recent experiments with .50-cal weapons has provided a major impetus for firearms manufacturers in the USA.

PSG-1

The PSG-1 is one of the world's most accurate sniper weapons, and consequently is much used by elite counter-terrorist and hostage-rescue forces. It was developed by Heckler & Koch from its globally successful G3 assault rifle but fitted with a much heavier barrel and calibrated to much greater accuracy. Like the G3, it fires the 7.62 x 51-mm NATO round and has a functional sniping range of around 800m (2624ft). The PSG-1 is in heavy use with the German police and rescue squads.

Accuracy

The PSG-1 has a formidable reputation for accuracy. Its ability to hit small targets consistently over long range is tested by putting 50 rounds of match ammunition into an 80mm (3.187in) circle at 300m (984ft) (this can be done with some speed as the PSG-1 is a semi-automatic rifle). This distance is an optimal sniping range, though the PSG-1 can handle distances up to 800m (2624ft)

Construction

The PSG-1 is made to be absolutely solid during firing, this meaning that nothing moves between rounds that will impair accuracy of shooting. The barrel and receiver assembly are virtually locked together to minimize movements between parts, and the barrel itself is of heavyweight construction to minimize vibration and heat build-up during firing. The steel outer surface of the receiver is nitro-carburized to increase its surface hardness and resist wear.

Accessories

When shipped, the PSG-1 comes with a range of accessories to help the maintenance, protection and performance of the weapon. It has its own case made of aluminium alloy with a custom-made foam fitted interior. It also comes with spare magazines, and adjustable sling, a cleaning kit, and a selection of essential tools for maintenance and sighting.

Below right: Night sights allow the sniper to take advantage of his long-range accuracy 24 hours a day. Hiding the muzzle flash is much more difficult, but most sniper kills in Vietnam were achieved at night at ranges of under 200 metres.

Left: British soldiers train on the Boys .55-cal anti-tank rifle. Most armies fielded such weapons during the 1930s until they were rendered obsolete by heavier tank armour, but their relatively long range led some soldiers to experiment with them as anti-personnel weapons. After the war, Finnish anti-tank rifles were even exported to the USA as 'varmint guns'.

Above: The full selection of .50-cal (12.7-mm×99) ammo is shown from left to right. **Ball** is the standard anti-personnel round and is usually mixed in with tracer in a machine-gun belt. The **tracer** round is used to correct the fall of shot when fired from a machine-gun. **Armour-piercing** is used for hard targets such as APCs, light tanks and bunkers. **Incendiary** is used for engaging soft-skinned vehicles such as trucks that will burn nicely. **Armour-piercing incendiary** gives the best of both worlds, and is very effective on helicopters. Finally, **armour-piercing tracer incendiary** is used in machine-guns and as blanks for training.

Right: The business end of the M2 Browning .50-cal machine-gun. The cartridge might be 60 years old and unsuited to sniping, but it was with just such a gun that Carlos Hathcock shot two Viet Cong at 2,500 yards.

Big 50s

In addition to the McMillan illustrated in the centrefold, there are three other .50-calibre rifles currently available. **The Barrett light 50** (above) is a semi-automatic rifle with an 11-round detachable magazine. The **Research Armament Industries Model 500** (top right) is a single-shot bolt action weapon that has a free floating barrel to increase its accuracy. The **Haskins .50-cal**

War II to the Falklands. In Vietnam, its range of nearly 3000 metres led US Marine sniper Carlos Hathcock to pioneer the use of the M2 as a sniper weapon.

Sniper machine-guns

Using an M2 machine-gun, Hathcock achieved his longest-range kill: hitting two Viet Cong guerrillas at 2500 metres. But an M2, mounted on its tripod, is over 1.6 metres long and weighs 40kg, which restricts it to static positions. However, the idea caught on and .50-calibre sniper rifles have begun to appear. It soon became obvious

that the basic .50-cal ammunition was not ideal for sniping – after all, it is designed for rapid fire from a machine-gun. Sniper grade ammunition is now available and tailored for many different purposes.

Weapons like the McMillan or Barrett M82 are still very heavy. They have to be to manage the fearsome recoil forces, but at up to 15kg in weight they are still manageable. The bullets weigh over 40 grams – more than four times the weight of a standard 7.62-mm round. Travelling at nearly 900 metres per second, their destructive power is exceeded only by a

20-mm cannon. .50-cal armour-piercing rounds will penetrate most military vehicles short of a main battle tank.

Shooting vehicles

The .50-cal sniper rifle does more than extend the range of the sniper: he can now take on vehicles or deal with targets inside parked aircraft or other cover. And few targets are going to walk away after a hit from a 40-g heavy alloy-cored streamlined bullet with explosive incendiary filler.

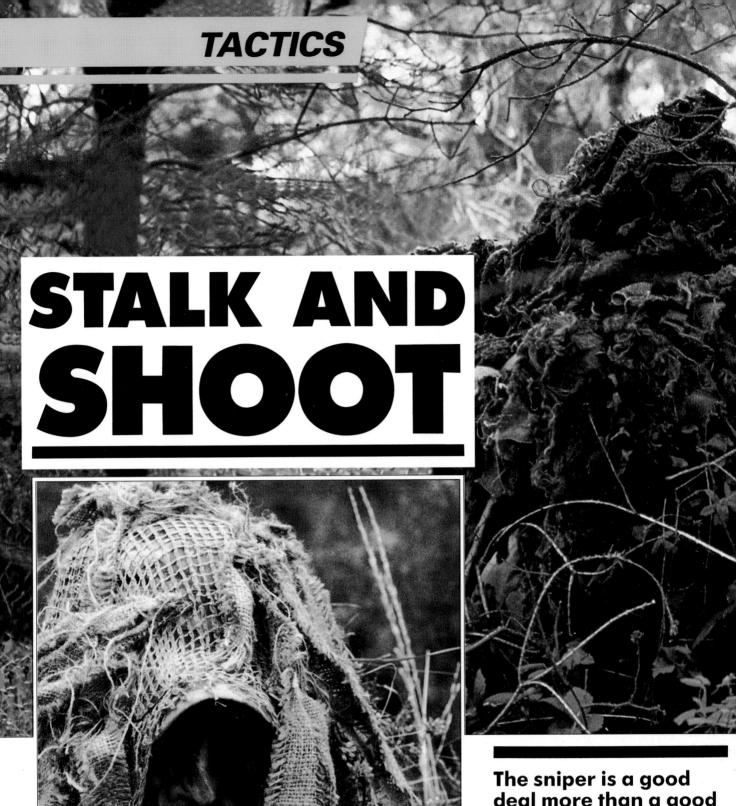

STALK AND SHOOT

Top: Not a shambling mound of compost but an expertly cammed up sniper breaking cover for a shot. The suit he wears breaks up the outline of the body and rifle, making it hard to distinguish him from the surrounding vegetation.

Above: The face of concentration. The sniper is a unique soldier who must combine superb fitness with great intelligence as well as an ability to hit a man-size target at over 1000 metres – something that appears not much larger than a pin.

The sniper is a good deal more than a good shot with a nice rifle: he is a complete weapon system, as important to the infantry company as MILAN or sustained-fire machine-guns.

"A sniper is an infantry soldier who is an expert marksman and observer, with the ability to locate an enemy, however well concealed, and then stalk or lie in wait to kill him with one round. He is able to observe, interpret and accurately report enemy movement. He can observe without

Sights

The PSG-1 is unlike many other sniping rifles in that its sight fittings are designed for one sight only: the Hensoldt 6 x 42 optical sight. The Hensoldt sight is configured for use up to about 600m, but it will exceed that with resighting, and it gives a clear and sharp sight picture even in low light conditions through illuminated cross hairs. No iron sights are fitted as backup to the PSG-1 as it is almost exclusively used as a police weapon which avoids the hard knocks of military users.

Adjustable features

The PSG-1 is designed to be adjusted to the shooter's own body dimensions, and thus improve the steady control of the weapon. The cheek rest, stock length and drop of butt can be adjusted to fit the operator's shoulder and face, and the supporting tripod can be fixed at the required height. The trigger also has a variable-width feature, and the pistol grip's palm shelf is fully adjustable.

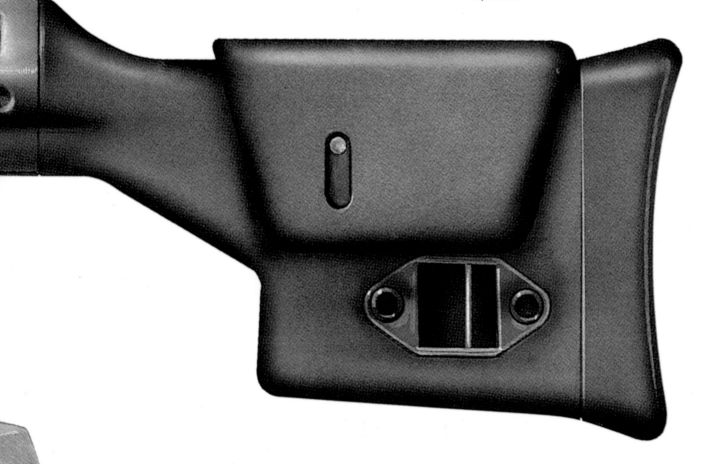

Cost prohibitions

The PSG-1 is a superb sniper weapon, but it is one that comes with a hefty price tag. In today's prices (2001) the rifle costs around $9300 (£5,800). This price tag is one of the factors that has stopped the PSG-1 being adopted more comprehensively by the world's special forces and police agencies, and its main customers are within Germany itself.

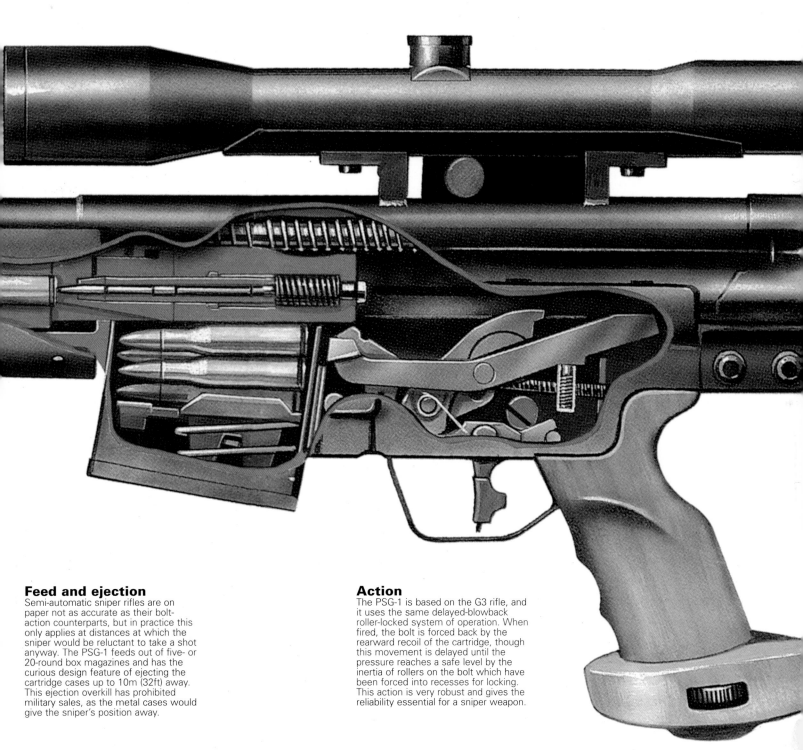

Feed and ejection

Semi-automatic sniper rifles are on paper not as accurate as their bolt-action counterparts, but in practice this only applies at distances at which the sniper would be reluctant to take a shot anyway. The PSG-1 feeds out of five- or 20-round box magazines and has the curious design feature of ejecting the cartridge cases up to 10m (32ft) away. This ejection overkill has prohibited military sales, as the metal cases would give the sniper's position away.

Action

The PSG-1 is based on the G3 rifle, and it uses the same delayed-blowback roller-locked system of operation. When fired, the bolt is forced back by the rearward recoil of the cartridge, though this movement is delayed until the pressure reaches a safe level by the inertia of rollers on the bolt which have been forced into recesses for locking. This action is very robust and gives the reliability essential for a sniper weapon.

2 Tactics

The sniper team usually operates with one member down, covering and observing while the other moves forward to the next position. All movements are made slowly to avoid being noticed, but if the snipers are too slow in the approach the target might move off, so if there is a good deal of open ground to cover to get within range of the target they will have to take risks early in order to leave time for hours of crawling inches at a time when close to the enemy. The sniper then decides at what range he can take the shot and guarantee a kill. If he is spotted, is there a chance of withdrawal?

Making a break for it. Confident the ground is clear, the sniper makes a quick dash.

Right, inset: Meticulous planning and a well thought out, solid plan are the keys to a successful mission. Often given only the roughest outline, the sniper must be able to select his own route in and out and interpret whatever intelligence he is given. In the end it is up to him: the mission makes or breaks on his initiative alone.

Below right: Kept to the barest minimum, the kit of a sniper is designed to be carried on the person. It is important that the equipment is non-reflective and will not jangle as he stalks his prey.

being observed and kill without being killed."

That is how the British Army describes the sniper. There is a lot more to it than just being able to hit a man-sized target in the head at 600 metres.

Master of camouflage

The sniper must be excellent at fieldcraft. He must be a master of camouflage and concealment. He must be able to map-read to the extent that he can instantly visualise the ground from the map, so that he can select the best route to approach. He must be able to stalk the target by manoeuvring unseen into a good firing position that will leave him with a clear shot and an escape route if required. He must be able to accurately assess the distance to the target and use his brain like a computer to calculate just where the point of aim should be to allow for the range and perhaps wind.

A couple of well-positioned snipers can hold up a whole enemy infantry company by pre-senting the threat of death every time an enemy shows his head above the parapet of his trench or cover. But the sniper is not there only to kill the enemy and deny him freedom of movement. He is of enormous value as a trained and concealed observer. Put out well forward of a company in defence, he can provide early warning of an enemy approach and report accurately on what he has seen.

1 Planning

Snipers usually operate in pairs, known as a 'sniper team'. Once the team is briefed, it is up to them how they will do the job. The first task is to make a thorough study of all the available maps and air photographs. The team wants a concealed route in to a firing point that will have a good, clear view of the target between 600 and 800 metres away, and if possible they should have a covered withdrawal route. If they get the chance, they will recce the first few legs of the route in. For added concealment, they may decide to make the approach to the area of the firing point at night.

3 The stalk

When the route is planned, the ground is divided up into bounds. Before moving into cover, the sniper carefully scans the ground ahead for enemy. Will he have to crawl all the way? Is there dead ground between him and any potential observer that will allow him to monkey-run or even run doubled over? He picks out points along the route to his next covered observation position to help navigate. It is very easy to become disorientated when crawling in thick cover, and if he sticks his head up to check his position he could alert the enemy and bring a hail of suppressive machine-gun fire in his direction.

Left: Often crawling several kilometres across rough, broken terrain and through thorn bushes requires skill and determination.

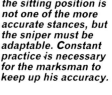

4 Choosing a firing point

The idea is to kill the enemy with one shot without being seen. Use of binoculars and scout telescope enable the sniper to observe the target and select the best point to fire from. Ideally this would offer a good view of the target area, cover from fire and view, and a withdrawal route if things get hot. The sniper should recce a number of secondary positions from which he can fire again or get a better arc of observation. He may have to occupy his firing position, without moving, for hours or even days to get the right target.

Left: The position chosen must command an excellent view of the target area. Personal comfort comes second to the mission's success, as can be seen by the bramble bush hide chosen here.

5 Target selection

First priority targets are enemy commanders. They can be easily distinguished by the number of radio antennas on their armoured vehicle. Snipers are experts: they know where that vehicle will be in an armoured column, they know which hatch the commander will appear from, and they know what differences in uniform distinguish the officers from the soldiers. Second priority are the radio operators who could call in artillery or inform higher command. The sniper will then try for troops who are especially dangerous because of the weapons they carry — enemy snipers, machine-gun teams, anti-tank gunners   etc.

Above: Shooting from the sitting position is not one of the more accurate stances, but the sniper must be adaptable. Constant practice is necessary for the marksman to keep up his accuracy.

Right: Delivering the goods. In the end, it is up to the judgement of the sniper who he kills, but high-value targets are a priority.

Right: Not even the expert and highly trained sniper can get away without digging in. In defence he will construct a hide well forward. From this position the sniper team will be able to pass back information on enemy movements and intentions in plenty of time to warn the defenders of the enemy approach.

6 The shoot

The sniper will be trying to get a head shot at 600 metres or a chest cavity shot from 600 to 1300 metres. When he locates a good target, he estimates the range, assesses the wind and aims off accordingly. After firing, he will check through the scope to confirm the kill. At this point he is at his most vulnerable. The enemy is likely to have a rough idea of his range and direction because of the shot, and they will start firing bursts of machine-gun fire into all the likely areas of concealment, with perhaps a few rockets and mortar rounds for good measure.

7 The sniper in defence

In defence, snipers are deployed in hides well forward of the main defensive position. Their task is not to kill the enemy with rifle fire but to report accurately on enemy activity and get that information back. They are also useful for harassing enemy recce patrols, so denying the enemy vital information about their main defensive position. When the enemy attacks, the snipers can kill commanders, force tanks to close down, and call in artillery.

This is the story of one mission undertaken by two snipers from the US Marine Corps. Their enemy was an elusive Viet Cong sniper who had killed several Americans in a fire base using a Soviet Mosin-Nagant rifle.

'ONE SHOT, ONE KILL'

US Marine Snipers in Vietnam

By mid-afternoon, Hathcock and Burke had moved to the top of the draw where it flattened into a saddle on the ridge. As the two men pushed forward, they began to notice birds pecking and scratching through the leaves. Above them, on lower branches, other birds sat and twittered. Below, in the draw, more birds gathered.

Hathcock took a closer look with the binoculars and saw what had attracted the many birds – rice. Someone had scattered rice and the birds, by their presence, created a natural early warning system that would alert the communist sniper to the arrival of an intruder. The man deserved respect for his cunning.

Once positioned, Hathcock took a branch and tossed it into the flock of birds. The sudden stir of wings flying up to the higher branches in the forest echoed down to where the small brown man lay behind his Mosin-Nagant rifle. A wild pig or big car might have sent the birds skyward, but another person might have done so too.

Crawling forward

The two Marines scrambled down the saddle and into the thick cover the draw offered. They dropped to their bellies and began to quietly crawl up the ridge to where the enemy sniper had passed on his trek to their former hide.

The crack and thud of the Marines scrambling into the draw told the NVA sniper that his quarry had flown. It was frustrating. He crept up the hill and examined the spot where the Americans had lain. Then he looked across the saddle and surveyed the field of fire his enemy had covered. It looked good.

Meanwhile the Marines had pushed an inch at a time through the low vines and bushes to where the ridge met the saddle. They were at the opposite end of their former field of fire.

"He's got to be here," Hathcock thought after searching every conceivable hide and seeing nothing. From his low, prone

*Above: A US Marine Corps sniper
from 1st Battalion, 3rd Marine
Regiment is shown in action
during Operation Virginia Ridge,
1969. He is using a Remington 700
hunting rifle with a telescopic
sight.*

*Left: The US Marines adopted the
heavy-barrelled Remington as their
standard sniper rifle, but many
shooters used big game rifles of
their own choice. These Army
snipers use 'accurised' M14s.*

*Above: The long-range killing
power of the sniper could not
always be exploited in the dense
terrain of Vietnam. Most kills were
achieved at under 150 metres: well
within the effective range of enemy
assault rifles.*

The US Marines' M40 sniper rifle produced by Remington has a five-round internal magazine. Weighing 6.5kg, it fires 7.62-mmx51 rounds with a muzzle velocity of 777 metres per second. The scope provides x10 magnification.

Left: A Starlight scope turned the standard M16 into a perfectly effective sniper weapon during the hours of darkness. It was a far better solution to enemy infiltration than the all-too common 'Mad Minute'.

position, he could see only the flat front angle that the rotten log and rock presented. "Where could he be?"

A large tree grew to the Marine sniper's left and offered enough cover to allow him to raise himself to a sitting position and possibly see behind the rock and log. Grabbing round the tree with his right hand and clutching the rifle with his left, Hathcock began to work his way up the tree's trunk to where he could sit and point his rifle scope at a high enough angle to see if his adversary had indeed moved into the Marines' vacated hide.

Hathcock had almost positioned himself and was about to work his legs into a cross-ankle position when the ground gave way beneath the edges of his boot soles and he sat hard, crunching twigs with a noisy plop.

The brown man who hid behind the rotted log peered through his scope and saw the sudden flash of movement. He had the American in his sights. And like the old fisherman who, after trying time after time to hook that grandfather trout, finally sees the great silver-and-green fish nipping at his lure, only to yank too soon and misses his catch, the dark-faced man jerked his rifle's trigger, bucking his shot wide and low.

Near miss

The sudden crack of rifle fire sent a surge of adrenalin through Hathcock's system. He raised his rifle and put the cross hairs on the log, where he saw the dark green flash of the enemy sniper disappear behind the foliage that hid his hide. "Damn!" Hathcock said under his breath.

Both snipers could hear the brush breaking as their enemy crashed his way through the woodland. They too jumped to their feet and hurried along the hilltop to a ridge that sloped to the forest below, and there Hathcock saw a gully where the run-off from the rain had eroded a route of escape for their enemy.

"Get down," he told Burke, as they crawled to the edge of the tree line, near the top of the ridge. "Bet you everything I own that he's in that gully."

Resting on his elbows, Burke scanned the full length of the gully with his binoculars, while Hathcock lay on his side prone behind his Winchester, looking for the slight flash or motion that would reveal his quarry.

They watched the long gully for an hour without seeing anything, yet Hathcock felt certain that their

Right: The sniper's role is not just the elimination of key enemy personnel. His ability to stalk unseen, close to the enemy, makes him an ideal observer.

Above: Experienced troops swapped their steel helmets for fatigue caps which did not muffle their hearing. Their shape was also much easier to disguise.

Below: Sniper teams often joined large patrols, dropping behind unnoticed to lie up overnight ready to ambush unsuspecting Viet Cong. Experience showed that even the VC spying system could not detect the fact that a 40-man patrol had only 38 men when it returned to base.

man had not fled, but hid in waiting for them.

The enemy sniper slowly searched each tree trunk. As he trained his binoculars again at the top of the hill where the trees met the crest of the gap, something caught his eye. The little man squeezed his eyes shut and looked again through his binoculars, squinting to see through the blinding rays of the low sun. "I think maybe I have found you, my young warrior."

In a smooth and deliberate motion, the NVA sniper raised his rifle from the gully and tucked it into his shoulder, steadying it with his left hand, which he rested on the ground above the trench. He concentrated on the pointed sight post inside the scope, but his target disappeared in the sun's glare, causing him to tilt and cant the weapon as he tried to pinpoint the Marine through the small scope and kill him.

"What's that?" Hathcock said, catching a flash of light in his scope.

Telltale glint

Carefully, Hathcock centred the scope's reticle on the glimmer of reflected sunlight. He released his breath and let the cross hairs settle on the target, and, as they settled, his .30-06 cracked down the hill, echoing through the wide,

treeless gap.

"Holy shit, Sergeant Hathcock! You got him!" Burke said as the glimmer disappeared and revealed the now dead man, whose body had bounded against the opposite side of the gully when the bullet struck.

Hathcock smiled at his partner and said, "One shot – one kill."

Burke reached the body first. "Nobody is gonna believe this unless they see it. Look at that. You put the round straight through his scope!"

Hathcock took the Russian-made sniper rifle from his partner and looked down the hollow tube of a telescopic sight that had had the glass blown from it as the bullet entered the enemy sniper's head through his eye.

"Burke, I just had a scary thought. He had to be sighting his rifle right at me for my bullet to pass clean through his scope and get him in the eye like that. When you get down to it, the only difference between me and him is that I got to the trigger first."

With the last remaining daylight, Hathcock sat next to the man's body and marked the exact position on his map. As for the rifle, its lensless scope and bloody stock were a reminder to Hathcock of how close he had come to losing this duel, and he carried it away with him.

A soldier of the Italian Alpini
mountain warfare unit on exercise
in 1992. The rifle is the 7.62-mm
Beretta BM59. Designed for the
Alpini, it features a folding stock
and a trigger which can be used
when wearing ski gloves.

A Spanish GEO sniper takes aim during hostage-rescue training. The soldier is taking aim with a PSG-1 sniper rifle, which is a semi-automatic weapon. Usually, a bolt-action rifle is chosen for sniping.

In service from 1993, the 9-mm Browning BDA9 double-action pistol is an excellent hand weapon. Its double-stacked magazine holds 14 rounds, it has an ambidextrous cocking lever, and the grip is shaped for double-handed use.

COMBAT HANDGUNS

The handgun does not win battles, but it saves the lives of those in battle. As an instrument of self-defence it may not be seen as very important by military planners, but to the men on the ground their pistol may be all that is going to come between them and oblivion.

The machine-gun's barrel was overheating badly. But the Viet Cong were pressing home their assault, and there was no time to change it. Flares cast their eerie light over the battlefield, silhouetting hundreds of scurrying figures in front of the American positions. The Viet Cong charge took the gunners by surprise, but a long burst of fire cut most of them down before the gun jammed.

The gunner scorched his fingers, clawing frantically at the now silent weapon while the last VC soldier ran towards him, levelling his AK. Then the silence was broken by the loud bark of a .45-calibre pistol. The VC toppled to the ground as the gunner emptied a full seven-round clip at him.

The Colt M1911 .45-calibre pistol was the last-ditch weapon of American servicemen from World War I to Vietnam. A chunky handful of a gun, its fat, stubby bullets soon earned the reputation of a man-stopper. It was issued to officers but saw most of its action in the hands of weapons crew – machine-gunners, mortar teams, soldiers with grenade-launchers. Such men were already carrying

This is the classic situation in which you need a pistol. If your main weapon fails for whatever reason, you can reach for your weapon (in this case a Browning High Power) to save your life.

too much to add a rifle to their load, and the .45 pistol became their final insurance.

The military use of the handgun is not confined to the army. Since the first aircraft flew into battle, pilots have carried pistols. In World War I, they were not only intended for the enemy. Flying airplanes with vulnerable petrol engines and not equipped with parachutes, many World War I pilots died agonising deaths in aircraft that burned all the way down. One of Britain's greatest fighter pilots, Mick Mannock, quietly admitted that if his aircraft caught fire, he would reach for his revolver and blow out his brains.

Pilot's weapons

Pilots liable to be shot down behind enemy lines have continued to carry handguns. While some paid little attention to them, others have become very enthusiastic. In Vietnam Huey Cobra gunship pilot Hugh Mills even carried two: a Colt .45 in a shoulder holster with five spare magazines, plus a Smith & Wesson .38 snub-nose on his belt. This additional weapon was not a service issue and reflects a common practice among certain officers in all forces to supplement their personal armoury. Hence the .357 Magnum carried by at least one officer of the Parachute Regiment in the Falk-

FLASHBACK

Young Winston (from the film of the same name) shoots his way out of a nasty corner at the Battle of Omdurman with a Mauser.

Swords and pistols

Army officers started to carry pistols during the 17th century. They were one of the main cavalry weapons at that time; during the English Civil War mounted troops often carried up to half a dozen pistols. But it was not until the mid-19th century that the pistol became really effective as a military weapon. Even then, its very short range restricted it to officers and cavalrymen, who found a sturdy handgun better than a sword in hand-to-hand fighting. In the last years of the 19th century British troops fought fanatical tribal warriors in the Sudan and American soldiers defeated equally determined irregular opponents in the Philippines. Both armies decided that they needed more powerful ammunition to deal with such fierce enemies – light .38-calibre rounds merely made them angry. In Britain this led to the series of powerful .455-in Webley revolvers, and the US Army adopted the Colt .45. These were in service by 1914.

The FN Browning High Power pistol is the most extensively used military pistol in the world, as well as being widely distributed for commercial sale. It was developed by John Browning and was introduced in 1935.

lands campaign.

Since World War II, all armies have relied on semi-automatic pistols rather than revolvers. Indeed, Britain was the only major European power to retain a revolver as the issue sidearm after the 1930s. Semi-automatic weapons like the Colt .45 and the Luger had proven their power and reliability during World War I. Quicker to reload, offering a high magazine capacity and, in some cases, safer to carry, semi-autos made better military sense. In 1935 the appearance of the Browning High Power with its 13-round

COMBAT HANDGUNS Reference File

167

BELGIUM

Browning High Power 9-mm pistol

Used by both sides during World War II, the Browning 9-mm pistol remains the standard service sidearm of the British Army and is still used by over 50 countries today. The name is misleading – it is no more high-powered than any other 9-mm pistol. It was first applied to the Browning by the Belgian army when it adopted it as the Model 35 in 1935: it referred to it as the 'Grand Puissance' because it was more powerful than anything it had previously used.

John Browning started work on the High Power after he designed the Colt M1911, and the weapon built on his experience with the famous .45. The High Power adopted a different method of unlocking the barrel from the slide,

The Browning is still a solid performer. This civilian version features high-visibility adjustable sights, which greatly increase the pistol's potential accuracy.

relying on a cam system instead of the swinging link.

The High Power was developed by John Browning at Fabrique National where work continued on the project after his death in 1926. The Belgian factories were overrun by the Germans in 1940 and it remained in production for the Wehrmacht and SS. But some of the designers escaped, and it entered limited production in England and Canada. After the war the

Browning practically cornered the market in service handguns, and it has been manufactured under licence in several countries.

Specification
Browning High Power
Calibre: 9-mm Parabellum

Feed: 13-round magazine
Weight: 1 kg with full magazine
Length: 200 mm
Barrel length: 118 mm
Sights: blade foresight, square notch rearsight
Muzzle velocity: 350 metres per second

Right: The problem with pistol cartridges is their lack of lethality, but the last few years has seen the development of some very high-powered handgun rounds such as the truly devastating, 10-mm Auto, fired from a Colt Delta Elite. It shoots flatter and hits harder but unfortunately the recoil takes some taming!

Below: The Walther P38 took over from the Luger as the official sidearm of the German armed forces during World War II. It was developed from earlier Walther double-action designs, the models PP and PPK, except this weapon was in a serious calibre – 9-mm Parabellum.

magazine made the traditional six-shot revolver obsolete as a military weapon.

The Colt .45, introduced in 1911, was only officially retired in 1985 when the US Army adopted the Beretta 92F under the designation M9 9-mm pistol. The longevity of the Colt is testimony both to the brilliance of John Browning's design, and the slow pace of pistol development. The system of operation he developed at the turn of the century has remained in common use even in the latest pistols produced during the 1980s. For example, the Ruger P85 9-mm pistol – a weapon designed from scratch, rather than a development of an existing type – still uses the tilting barrel design that Browning would instantly recognise.

Recoil energy

Military semi-automatic pistols work by harnessing the recoil forces generated by firing a bullet. The explosion of the cartridge sends the bullet up the barrel and exerts an equal force in the other direction. Different weapons deal with this force in several ways, but all use the energy to drive back the slide surrounding the barrel. This movement pulls out the empty cartridge case, ejecting it from the gun. A strong spring under the barrel is compressed by the slide's rearward movement and eventually drives it forward again. During the return journey, the top round in the magazine is stripped off and fed into the chamber. The cycle is now ready to begin again.

The differences between modern pistols stem from the various methods used to control the recoil forces. During the 1970s, as police forces joined the military in buying new pistols, the demand for advanced safety systems led to new mechanisms appearing. They serve to prevent the weapon firing accidentally if dropped on a hard surface or otherwise mis-used. In fact, several weapons including both the Colt M1911 and the Luger had grip safeties fitted: the guns cannot fire unless a hand is physically holding down a lever

---

168

GERMANY

Walther P1 9-mm pistol

This is another veteran handgun, the modern production version of the wartime German P38. In service with the German Army and exported to several nations including Chile and Portugal, the P1 is also offered in a silenced version for Special Forces. The original P38 was the victor in a German Army competition in the mid-1930s to find a replacement for the famous Luger pistol which had been in service since 1908. By the end of World War II, it is estimated that about one million P38s had been manufactured. The pistol proved highly successful and served on all fronts during the war. When the West German army was formed during the 1950s, it examined the alternatives and concluded that it

This is a chopped P38, which is a little hard to handle. After the war the new production P38s were renamed the P1 for the new West German army.

wanted the P38 as its standard service pistol.

Re-designated P1, built with an alloy frame and a few minor alterations, the P38 returned to production in 1957. Compared with its commercial rivals, it lacks the massive magazines which have become increasingly fashionable. Its worst feature is the magazine catch – still sited at the heel of the butt, which makes for a slower reload than a thumb-operated button on the side. But

it does have a double-action trigger, allowing it to be carried 'locked and cocked', and thus brought into action with the minimum of delay.

Specification
Walther P1 9-mm pistol
Calibre: 9-mm Parabellum

Feed: 8-round detachable box
Weight: 772 g unloaded; 960 g loaded
Length: 218 mm
Barrel length: 124 mm
Sights: blade foresight; 'U' notch rearsight
Muzzle velocity: 350 metres per second

John Browning's locking system

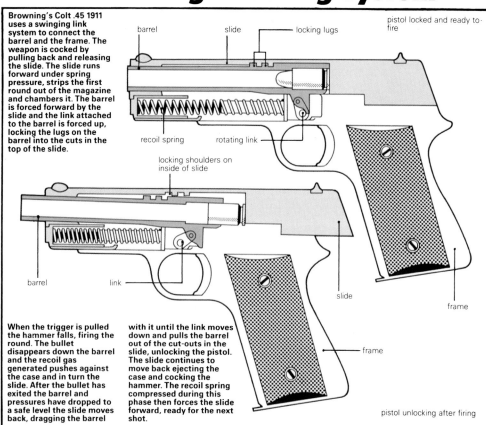

Browning's Colt .45 1911 uses a swinging link system to connect the barrel and the frame. The weapon is cocked by pulling back and releasing the slide. The slide runs forward under spring pressure, strips the first round out of the magazine and chambers it. The barrel is forced forward by the slide and the link attached to the barrel is forced up, locking the lugs on the barrel into the cuts in the top of the slide.

barrel · slide · locking lugs · pistol locked and ready to fire

recoil spring · rotating link

locking shoulders on inside of slide

barrel · link · slide · frame

frame

pistol unlocking after firing

When the trigger is pulled the hammer falls, firing the round. The bullet disappears down the barrel and the recoil gas generated pushes against the case and in turn the slide. After the bullet has exited the barrel and pressures have dropped to a safe level the slide moves back, dragging the barrel

with it until the link moves down and pulls the barrel out of the cut-outs in the slide, unlocking the pistol. The slide continues to move back ejecting the case and cocking the hammer. The recoil spring compressed during this phase then forces the slide forward, ready for the next shot.

mounted in the butt.

The bewildering range of semi-automatic pistols available today is not due to heavy demand from the military. Paramilitary forces, police agencies and civilian target shooters have created a ready market for the numerous manufacturers. But although pistols are produced chambered for many different cartridges, only three have been in widespread military service since 1945. The most popular choice of military pistol round is the 9-mm Parabellum, also known as the 9-mm Luger. Also used by most sub-machine guns, it has been the standard western European round since before World War II.

Common cartridges

The Soviets never adopted it, relying on their old 7.62-mm round until the 1950s. Then they produced the 9-mm Makarov pistol with a 9-mm bullet of their own to go with it. The third military pistol cartridge still commonly encountered is the famous .45 ACP (Automatic Colt Pistol), produced for the M1911. Although the US Army has adopted the M9 9-mm, the hundreds of thousands of M1911s still in service and the countless numbers in private hands ensure the survival of this historic cartridge.

169

AUSTRIA

Glock 9-mm pistol

This is the standard pistol of the Austrian army and has been acquired by several NATO Special Forces units. The designers' concern to keep certain aspects of the weapon secret prevented them entering it in the US Army pistol trials, and so denied the pistol the chance of a much wider market. The Glock is unusual in that it is constructed mainly from plastic. The receiver is a monocoque design, built from a tough polymer that can survive up to 200 degrees Centigrade. This makes the weapon very light: good news for the soldier, but off-putting to the 'old school', who remained suspicious about a black plastic gun no heavier than a water pistol.

The Glock even managed to confuse

civilian practical pistol shooters, who are used to seeing an external safety on a gun. In a sport in which safety is rightly emphasised, a visible safety device is an obvious advantage since an unsafe gun can be spotted immediately. The Glock confounds this by relying on internal safety mechanisms that keep the weapon safe between shots. These are released by pressure on the trigger: only a correct trigger pull will allow the weapon to fire.

The Glock's massive magazine capacity is an attraction to some military users who want a lot of firepower but without the bulk of a sub-machine gun. It is a robust weapon, its strength confirmed by numerous tests,

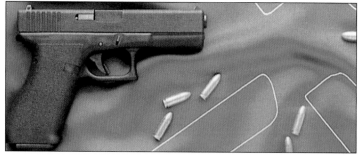

and it certainly makes a dramatic contrast to veteran handguns like the Browning or the Walther P1.

Specification
Glock 17 military pistol
Calibre: 9-mm Parabellum
Feed: 17-round magazine

Weight: 620 g empty; 870 g loaded
Length: 188 mm
Barrel length: 114 mm
Sights: blade foresight; notch rearsight
Muzzle velocity: 350 metres per second

170

GERMANY

Heckler & Koch P7

This was specifically designed for continental police forces, but was soon adopted by the West German army and various Special Forces units. Other military sales followed, to South America and Asia. Pistol safety and speed of operation are major police concerns, so H & K developed a novel squeeze-cocking system instead of a conventional safety catch: gripping the P7 pistol in the hand squeezes the bar along the front of the grip and frees the trigger. The gun cannot fire without being properly held in the hand, so a dropped gun will not go off even with a live round in the chamber. It is obviously quick into action since the user does not have to worry about releasing a safety catch.

The P7 was designed specifically for the West German police handgun trials carried out in the late 1970s. It is a very advanced pistol, with no manual safeties.

The P7 incorporates several other features that make it a successful military weapon. Although the grip is positioned at an angle to the barrel (essential for the user to hold the pistol properly), the magazine rises almost vertically. This helps make the feed very reliable, even when using

unusually shaped bullets. The P7 is available with either eight- or 13-round magazines. The former version is nearly 200 g lighter and 4 mm shorter.

Specification
P7M13 pistol
Calibre: 9-mm Parabellum

Feed: 13-round magazine
Weight: 780 g empty; 1135 g loaded
Length: 175 mm
Barrel length: 105 mm
Sights: adjustable blade foresights; adjustable rearsight
Muzzle velocity: 350 metres per second

The Professional's View:

Pistols

"**S**ome people think that shooting people with pistols is easy: one shot and 'bang' they're down and dead or completely out of it. It just is not like that. There are cases of people taking over 10 hits with a 9-mm and still having enough left to kill the other guy. The key to survival is good shot placement. That means hitting something vital and firing until he goes down and stays there. In turn, that means you have to train to achieve accuracy and speed under conditions of extreme stress. This takes time practising the right techniques in a realistic situation, and most of all truckloads of ammunition."

Lieutenant D. Ballantine, US police officer

The Browning High Power was produced with two sight options: the ordinary fixed type and the exotic adjustable tangent type, which had a frame slotted for the shoulder stock seen here. The 500-metre setting is very optimistic. The stock does not greatly improve accuracy.

171

SWITZERLAND

SIG-Sauer P220

Used by the Swiss army and acquired by police and various specialist military units, the P220 is one of a series of 9-mm pistols that enjoy a very high reputation. Swiss-made firearms have become renowned for their quality of manufacture and superb performance: unfortunately they also come with a massive price tag, which limits their appeal to wealthy police agencies or Special Forces. Even then, they can be trumped: the FBI used SIGs during the late 1980s while they evaluated a series of handguns and their ammunition. The new Smith & Wesson 10-mm pistol won.

The P220 is also available in .45 ACP 7.65-mm Parabellum, .38 Super, and .22 Long Rifle calibres. It has been

The early issue was a great pistol, ruined by a heel of the butt magazine release: this made a speed reload very slow. Subsequent models have thumb release catches.

followed by the similar P225, which won several police sales, and the 15-shot P226, which competed against the Beretta 92 for the US Army order. The P225 and P226 have their magazine releases sensibly sited where the firer's left thumb can hit them; the P220 retains the old-fashioned catch in the butt.

Specification
P220 9-mm pistol
Calibre: 9-mm Parabellum
Feed: 9-round magazine
Weight: 730 g empty
Length: 198 mm

Barrel length: 112 mm
Sights: blade foresight, notch rearsight
Muzzle velocity: 345 metres per second

172

Former USSR

Makarov 9-mm pistol

The Makarov is the standard Soviet military pistol, and has been supplied to most Warsaw Pact armies. It fires a different round to Western 9-mm weapons: the case is a millimetre shorter, and only one type of bullet has been produced. This is a 6-gram fully jacketed round, as opposed to the NATO standard 7.45-g 9-mm FMJ. The Makarov is essentially a copy of the Walther PP pistol. It is a double-action weapon: if the safety is applied after the weapon has been cocked, the hammer drops but the firing pin is blocked. The gun can then be carried safely. Flip off the safety and the gun can be fired without having to rack back the slide.

Manufactured from high-grade steel,

A nice pistol with a good trigger pull, quite unlike the rough and ready Tokarev TT 33 it has replaced. The problem is the round, which is not exactly a man-stopper.

it is well built and perfectly adequate for the Soviets' purposes. It is issued to Soviet officers above platoon commanders and carried by the crews of armoured vehicles. However, tank or APC crewmen in Afghanistan soon acquired paratroop versions of the AKM or AK-74 assault rifles, recognising the pistol's limitations as a last-ditch weapon against the Mujahideen. The Soviets have never regarded pistols as

important military weapons: Soviet soldiers armed with the Makarov are issued only with 16 rounds and a spare magazine.

Specification
Makarov 9-mm pistol
Calibre: 9-mm×18 Makarov

Feed: 8-round magazine
Weight: 750 g empty; 810 g loaded
Length: 160 mm
Barrel length: 96 mm
Sights: blade foresight; notch rearsight
Muzzle velocity: 315 metres per second

A member of the Jesse James gang was hit 16 times by round-nosed, soft lead bullets, and survived

Just as the change from 7.62-mm calibre rifles to 5.56-mm ones led to a lot of debate about 'stopping power', the US Army's abandonment of the .45 cartridge led to the same arguments. In the case of military pistols, there is no doubting the lethality of the massive 230-grain slugs fired from a Colt M1911. The universally accepted 9-mm Parabellum fires much smaller rounds – 100-115 grains, but at much higher velocities. Both will kill you; but the .45 is more likely to disable an opponent first. However, terms like 'knockdown power' and the popular image on TV of handguns blasting people off their feet are both complete fiction. No handgun – or service rifle – will knock anyone to the ground by the sheer force of the bullet.

Short range

While experienced pistol shooters can hit man-sized targets at 100 metres or more, the typical military user using a standard service weapon is only effective at 15-20 metres. This is not particularly important since the pistol is a secondary weapon. But it does leave the mortar team or other group of specialists vulnerable to enemy riflemen who could simply sit 100 metres away and shoot them down without reply. This problem has been tackled in the past by issuing shoulder stocks for pistols, turning them into small carbines and boosting their effective range to around 150-

200 metres. The Mauser C96 and Artillery Model Luger, with its 20-cm barrel, set the trend. Both were used by German machine-gun teams during World War I. The Browning High Power has also been issued with a stock and adjustable sights set up to 500 metres.

Ironically, the manufacturers of the famous Browning High Power have now developed a weapon designed to make all military pistols as obsolete as the sword. The P90 is a sub-machine gun type weapon firing a unique 5.7-mm bullet from a 50-round see-through plastic magazine. It has long been recognised that the pistol has more limitations than that of a short range. It requires a great deal of training and regular, weekly practice to become a tolerably good shot with a handgun.

But most soldiers issued with pistols have them as secondary weapons, and spend almost all their training time on their primary task. So when the machine-gun jams or the tank crewman escapes from his wrecked vehicle, he may find his pistol shooting is terminally rusty. The P90 is a shoulder-fired weapon with an effective range of 150 metres – and it is deliberately engineered to be idiot-proof. It gives someone with little training their best chance of doing some damage and protecting themselves in an emergency. After 150 years of distinguished service, the military pistol is seriously threatened by this revolutionary weapon.

Combat Comparison

The rest of the world adopted the 9-mm round as standard for pistols and SMGs years ago, but the Americans stuck to the old .45 for over 75 years before it was controversially replaced by the Beretta. This move has caused a storm among soldiers brought up with the Colt's legendary stopping power, but those in charge of procurement have argued that the old faithful is too loud and too difficult to train recruits with.

173 USA

Colt M1911 .45 Pistol

The Colt M1911 remains the greatest handgun of the 20th century. Its system of operation has been copied so widely that it is still the basis for most semi-automatic pistols in production today. The designation '.45' refers to the calibre of the cartridge: just over 11 mm across, it is a fat dustbin of a bullet, instantly more impressive than the 9-mm Parabellum when weighed in the hand. This chunky round was developed after US officers found their .38 revolvers did not always stop

The P90 is the way ahead for the military sidearm. For tank crews and the like it offers far more than a pistol, but the pistol will live on where concealment is required, in the police and anti-terrorist field.

charging Filipino tribesmen during the guerrilla war of 1898-9. Used by US troops in both world wars, Korea and Vietnam, the idea of replacing it was strongly opposed by some elements within the Army. But the US Army wanted to adopt a 9-mm pistol like every other NATO force, and have the advantages of large magazine capacity and the ability to safely carry a loaded gun. The .45 remains in production for the large civilian market in the USA and it remains a worldwide favourite for certain shooting competitions.

Specification
Colt .45 M1911A1 pistol
Calibre: .45 ACP
Feed: 7-round detachable magazine
Weight: 1.13 kg with empty magazine; 1.36 kg loaded
Length: 219 mm
Barrel length: 127 mm
Sights: blade foresight, 'U' notch rearsight
Muzzle velocity: 253 metres per second

The sights on the 1911 and the 1911A1 are really too small for combat use. Their only advantage is that it is difficult to break them. The Beretta has modern high-visibility sights with the proven three-dot system for rapid sight alignment in poor light conditions.

The Colt is single-action only. That means that pulling the trigger does nothing but drop the hammer. The weapon can be carried cocked and locked by the safety catch or hammer down on a live round in the chamber. In that case, you have to thumb back the hammer to fire the weapon. The Beretta, on the other hand, is double-action. Pulling the trigger both pulls the hammer back if it is not already there, and drops it.

The most universally used pistol and SMG cartridge is 9-mm Parabellum. It makes sense from a resupply point of view to have a pistol and SMG that fire the same ammo and there are very few .45 ACP SMGs in service. Having said that, the huge .45 240-grain bullet does far more damage than the 9-mm.

In battle, the extra magazine capacity of the Beretta represents a considerable advantage over the Colt. Larger frames for the Colt are available on the civilian market, which increase the magazine capacity.

 174 ITALY

Beretta 92 9-mm pistol

The Beretta 92 series of 9-mm pistols achieved the unthinkable in 1985. The Italian design triumphed over stiff competition to win the world's most coveted pistol order and become the US Army's new pistol. American troops had been equipped with the .45 calibre Colt M1911 since before World War I. By the 1970s, the age of the weapons in service was giving cause for concern and many people regarded the Colt design as obsolete. The search began for a replacement. After a tortuous series of trials, the Beretta was adopted in 1985 as the US Army's M9 9-mm pistol.

The Beretta's most obvious advantage over its predecessor is its large magazine capacity. Its 15-shot double-column magazine provides the soldier with twice as many rounds. The safety catch is ambidextrous, so a left-handed shooter has no difficulty. Other smart new features include the 'Bruniton' finish – a hard Teflon-like material that protects the metal surfaces. The magazine has an extended base offering a better grip, and the trigger guard front is flattened to allow the shooter's left fingers to fit around it for a two-handed grip. The use of 9-mm rounds brings the US forces into line with the rest of NATO, where this cartridge has been the standard pistol and sub-machine gun round since World War II.

The Beretta 92 has one weakness: some of the first batch supplied to the US Army were found to have cracked slides after several thousands of rounds. A catastrophic slide failure is a potentially lethal accident, and the result was a fresh round of tests. But the Army was satisfied with the M9's performance and production was resumed in 1989.

Specification
Beretta 92F/M9 9-mm pistol
Calibre: 9-mm Parabellum
Feed: 15-round detachable magazine
Weight: 950 g with empty magazine
Length: 217 mm
Barrel length: 125 mm
Sights: blade foresight, notched bar rearsight
Muzzle velocity: 390 metres per second

Right: *The first pistol that met with any commercial success was the Borchardt. It was intended for use with or without a shoulder stock, and worked well. Hugo Luger perfected the toggle action of the Borchardt in the famous Luger.*

A FISTFUL OF
FIREPOWER

The handgun is light, easy to carry and conceal, and is excellent for the task of self-defence. Pistols do not win battles, but they can occasionally save the lives of the men involved in the battle.

Above: The SAS are masters with a 9-mm Browning High Power. Unlike larger weapons, the rifle and SMG, the pistol is far more dependent on the skill of the user to be effective. The lead trooper carries a long-barrelled target model Browning.

Above: The first technically successful automatic pistol was marketed in Austria by the inventor Schönberger. As you can see, it was quite an odd beast that was dependent for its success on the development of a rimless cartridge case that could withstand the violent jerk of automatic extraction.

The idea of an automatic pistol was first discussed when in 1664 Sir Robert Moray gave a lecture to the Royal Society outlining his ideas of how such a weapon should work. It was novel stuff, and clearly too much for his fellow scientists. Getting from first principles to a production weapon that worked took well over 200 years!

The theory of the automatic pistol could not be realised until technology had caught up. Metals technology, in particular, had to wait for the invention of a reliable metallic pistol cartridge with smokeless powder.

The first commercially successful auto-loading pistol was designed in America but produced in Germany. Hugo Borchardt, the inventor, had earlier worked for Winchester Repeating Arms Company, but failed to interest any US firms in manufacturing his rather clumsy, though effective, toggle-locked breech weapon, which featured a detachable box magazine and stock. The Berlin-based company of Ludwig Loewe manufactured the weapon and the bottleneck cartridge designed for it; it was marketed in 1893.

Notably, one of Borchardt's assistants at the Loewe plant was one Herr George Luger. Herr Luger redesigned the toggle mechanism to produce the now world-famous Luger pistol, which was standard issue to the German military from 1908 to 1938.

The Mannlicher M1903 was designed to compete with the Mauser C96. The problem with this pistol, as with many early designs, was reliability. The pistol is a last-ditch weapon, so any failure can lead directly to the death of the owner. Reliability was one of the reasons that Britain stuck to revolvers when far superior automatics were on the market.

Below: Which would you rather have when faced with a horde of Mahdi's crazed Fuzzy-Wuzzies, or when clearing a trench on the Western Front: a sword or a superb Broomhandle Mauser 1898? Some versions were even made for automatic fire!

Above: The Old Faithful, from World War I to Vietnam. Here a US Marine blasts away at NVA positions with his Colt .45 1911A1 at Khe Sanh combat base in 1968.

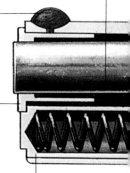

Barrel
Note how it locks into th slide. It is primarily designed to shoot GI ba ammo, not lead target loads.

Front sight
This is too small for really effective combat use; it is better to replace it with a high-visibility combat sight if the weapon is your own.

Barrel bushing
This supports the barrel and holds the plunger in place. Target bushings are available on Series 70 Colt Mk IVs and they do improve accuracy, but they have no place in combat shooting as tolerances are too tight for sustained reliability.

Plug plunger
Depress the front end of the plunger, 'the plug', in order to rotate the barrel bushing anti-clockwise at the start of the field strip. This is the piece you are most likely to lose as it is under strong spring pressure.

Inside the Colt .4

Colt's combat clas

Browning did have his flops on the road to the famous Colt .45 1911A1. In 1900 Colt introduced a new Browning automatic pistol in .38 calibre that was really fully automatic — one pull of the trigger and the entire magazine emptied. From this unique, if a touch impractical, design, Browning went on to produce the Colt .38 automatic pistol, which fired its own high-performance .38 auto cartridge.

The performance was so awesome that a bullet would penetrate 11 inches of pine! Big-game hunters of the time used to carry it as a back-up weapon. The bad

The Mauser pistol

The automatic pistol as a military weapon did not make an impression on the battlefield until 1895, when Mauser introduced the famous 7.63-mm military model. Hugo Borchardt was credited by Mauser for providing the 7.63-mm cartridge and some of the basic work on the pistol. It was peculiar in being clip-loaded, with the magazine forward of the trigger guard. This weapon was popular in both world wars and may have saved the life of the young Lieutenant Winston Churchill at the Battle of Omdurman in the Sudan. Selective fire versions with stocks were also available.

Right: The Luger became a design legend in spite of the fact that the trigger mechanism was over-complicated and the whole weapon was a little dirt-sensitive. This is the very collectable long-barrelled artillery model with a 32-round snail drum magazine and detachable stock.

Sig Sauer P226

The P226 was designed specifically to compete in the US Army pistol trials. Produced to Swiss standards of manufacture, it is possibly one of the finest double-action 9-mm autos available. It has a decocking lever for safely lowering the hammer on a loaded chamber and takes mags of 15 or 20 rounds.

FN Browning High Power Model 1935

The High Power is a little long in the tooth, but what it lacks in design sophistication it makes up for in quality and reliability. The original version is a single-action 13-shot auto with poor sights and controls compared to modern pistols, but this double-action version has recently been introduced by Fabrique Nationale in Belgium.

Jericho

Israel Military Industries have produced some of the world's best small arms, including the Uzi SMG and the Galil assault rifle. The Jericho is not quite in the same class, but it is solidly built and is available in a number of calibres, including the high-performance .41 Action Express.

Modern combat hang

Modern military handguns have grown in official popularity with the shift in the nature of the 'threat' from that of a conventional war in Europe to that of the bush fire war and terrorism: the pistol has a far greater role to play in counter-terrorism and counter-insurgency than in conventional operations. These pistols show that, despite differences in tactical doctrine, most armies want the same things from a military pistol — a common calibre, 9-mm Parabellum ammunition, large magazine capacity, simple and safe operation, double action, and high visibility sights. All non-Third World nations now use self-loading pistols rather than revolvers.

Beretta Model 84
This double-action pistol fires the much less powerful 9-mm short or .380 auto round, which is better suited to self-defence use. The magazine capacity of 13 rounds offers a degree of firepower not usually found in pocket pistols. It is, like all Beretta products, well made and finished and is aimed squarely at the European civilian and police market, where 9-mm short is seen as the smallest effective pistol calibre.

Ruger P85
This 9-mm double-action pistol is a hot contender for the US military pistol contract. The Americans simply could not believe that their scientists and testers could select a handgun that was not made in the USA — i.e. the Beretta; the Ruger is American-made, which may swing things in their favour for future pistol orders. Magazine capacity is 15 rounds.

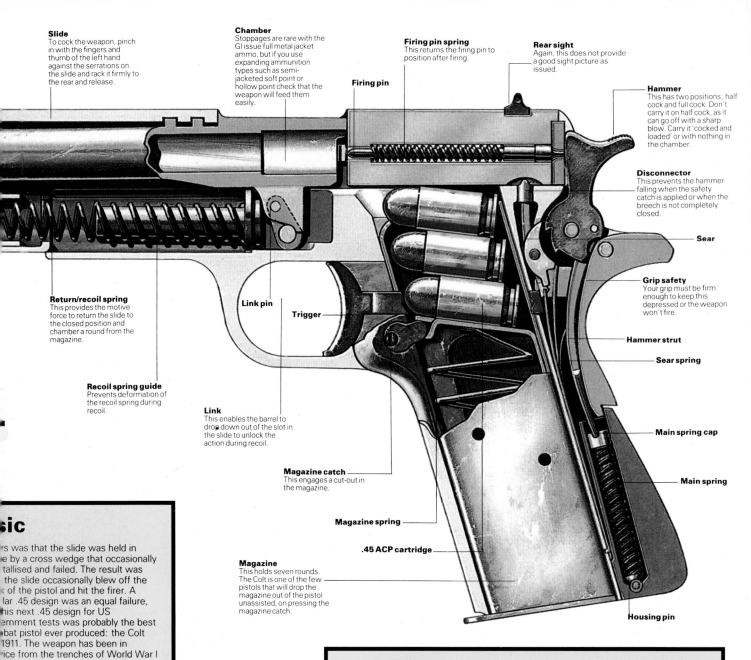

Slide
To cock the weapon, pinch in with the fingers and thumb of the left hand against the serrations on the slide and rack it firmly to the rear and release.

Chamber
Stoppages are rare with the GI issue full metal jacket ammo, but if you use expanding ammunition types such as semi-jacketed soft point or hollow point check that the weapon will feed them easily.

Firing pin spring
This returns the firing pin to position after firing.

Rear sight
Again, this does not provide a good sight picture as issued.

Firing pin

Hammer
This has two positions; half cock and full cock. Don't carry it on half cock, as it can go off with a sharp blow. Carry it 'cocked and loaded' or with nothing in the chamber.

Disconnector
This prevents the hammer falling when the safety catch is applied or when the breech is not completely closed.

Sear

Return/recoil spring
This provides the motive force to return the slide to the closed position and chamber a round from the magazine.

Link pin

Trigger

Grip safety
Your grip must be firm enough to keep this depressed or the weapon won't fire.

Hammer strut

Sear spring

Recoil spring guide
Prevents deformation of the recoil spring during recoil.

Link
This enables the barrel to drop down out of the slot in the slide to unlock the action during recoil.

Main spring cap

Magazine catch
This engages a cut-out in the magazine.

Main spring

Magazine spring

.45 ACP cartridge

Magazine
This holds seven rounds. The Colt is one of the few pistols that will drop the magazine out of the pistol unassisted, on pressing the magazine catch.

Housing pin

This Browning Model 1900 had the distinction of being the first of John Browning's designs to be produced at the FN plant in Belgium. It saw limited use as an official service pistol, but was privately purchased in thousands.

John Moses Browning: a legend in small-arms design

Browning was quite simply the most successful small-arms designer in history. Like many American inventors of the time, he had to go to Europe to get his first designs manufactured. His first design was a .32, or 7.65-mm, that became one of the most widely distributed pistol types in the world. The weapon was manufactured by Fabrique National in Belgium, currently the world's largest small-arms manufacturer.

IN FOCUS

World War I

The Great War was started with one of John Browning's excellent self-loading pistols; it shot Archduke Franz Ferdinand at Sarajevo.

The military had long recognised that the pistol was a weapon of defence, and so issued it only to officers and specialists. However, it slowly became clear, in the stalemate of trench warfare, that the people who really needed pistols were the front-line soldiers. The pistol offered firepower that could be quickly brought to bear in the close confines of a trench; an automatic pistol, and a sharpened entrenching tool, dagger or club, were the ideal weapons for this most primitive of warfares. Only when the first sub-machine guns appeared in late 1918 were weapons such as the Colt .45 1911A1 and the Luger, with its snail drum magazine, outgunned in close-quarter battle.

The British War Office had a habit of issuing pistols to all but those who really needed them. The Webley and Scott .455 automatics would have been far more gainfully employed in the hands of French raiding parties rather than these naval officers.

Above: Freikorps in Berlin 1919. In a world without an assault rifle or many SMGs, the Mauser offered a close-range advantage over those armed with a bolt-action rifle. Even with a stock these weapons are not particularly accurate by modern pistol standards. The magazine could only be clip-loaded on most models of Mauser C96, which made for slow and fiddly reloading.

Above: In the United States the Savage Arms Company entered a .45-calibre pistol with a peculiar hesitation lock for US Government evaluation in 1906. It lost badly to Browning's Colt. The design went on to become used in Savage's excellent pocket pistols.

Left: A pair of Webley and Scott automatics. The smaller of the two was standard issue to the Royal Navy from 1912. Some were fitted with stocks and issued to the Royal Flying Corps.

Walther P5

The P5 was designed using the very tough criteria laid down by the West German government when conducting trials for a replacement for the woefully inadequate Walther PP and PPK. The P5 was one of the few pistols that passed, and it has been adopted by several West German police forces. The magazine contains only eight rounds, but this is considered adequate for police use.

WINCHESTER. *Western.*
50 CENTER FIRE
PISTOL.
REVOLVER
CARTRIDGES
WARNING: Keep Out of Reach of Children

Star Firestar
Spain has a reputation for producing some poor-quality pistols, but Star has produced quality Colt lookalikes for years. The Firestar is slightly more innovative and is perhaps best suited to police use.

Star Model 30M
The standard pistol of the Spanish army, this 9-mm double-action pistol has some unique features. The ambidextrous safety catch, when applied, withdraws the firing pin into a tunnel out of the way of the hammer. This means that you can draw the pistol, pull the trigger and drop the hammer, and nothing happens. That could definitely be a problem as normal safeties lock the trigger, which acts as a reminder that you have the safety on! The weapon has a mag capacity of 15 rounds.

Brno CZ 85
Czechoslovakia has for many years had a highly efficient arms industry. The CZ 85, double-action and firing the 9-mm cartridge, has proved so popular that a Swiss company started manufacturing the weapon in order to get round an import ban on Warsaw Pact goods to the USA. The ban has now been lifted and vast quantities have been purchased worldwide.

The combat pistol in World War II

The American military went to considerable trouble to find out just how many enemy casualties had been inflicted with pistols during the course of the five years of World War II. The figure was so small that it was argued that the pistol was of no combat value. However, there are few soldiers who doubt the psychological value of having a pistol as a back-up weapon if your rifle fails.

The Americans used the excellent Colt .45 Government model, designed by John Browning. The British were stuck with some less-than-useful Webley revolvers, but substantial quantities of Browning High Power pistols were also used; its large magazine and ammunition shared with the Sten gun made the weapon popular for commando use. The Browning High Power is still in service today with the British Army.

Above: Although Walther produced some very advanced double-action designs the Germans soldiered on with the Luger, seen here in the hands of an SS mortar crewman.

Inset: The Lugers were slowly replaced with the Walther P 38, but the better weapon was definitely the Browning High Power. Substantial quantities were used by the Germans.

Post-war developments

Major developments have consisted of little more than improved materials, including, for instance, the use of plastics in the Glock pistol. Mechanisms have been refined to provide extra safety features without the need to operate any manual safeties, as in the case of the Heckler & Koch P7, and recoil has been reduced in some pistols, using the propellant gas of the cartridge, such as in the Steyr GB pistol.

However, no major advances in pistol design are expected until there are further advances in ammunition, plastics or metallurgical technology. It is testimony to the genius of John Moses Browning that after nine decades his original designs are almost unchanged.

Above and top: The Russian Tokarev TT33 (top) was basically the same as the Colt .45. It was more robust and fired the very powerful bottle-necked 7.62-mm pistol round. The Makarov that has replaced it is far more sophisticated.

Inside the H&K P7

The P7 was adopted by the German Army as the ultimate replacement for the Walther P1. The P7M13 is a modified version produced for the 1981 US JSSAP tests and is now marketed commercially.

Foresight

Rearsight
Able to be adjusted only for windage, the sights use the three-dot system for swift target acquisition.

Bolt

Striker

Polygonal rifling
This is claimed to reduce fouling and ease maintenance. The gun is designed only for full metal jacket factory ammunition. You can use unjacketed bullets but the P7 will need very thorough cleaning.

Gas mechanism
Part of the gases produced on firing are diverted through this vent, fractionally delaying the rearward movement of the slide.

Trigger
The trigger breaks at about 4½ lb.

13-round magazine
The M- designation after the P7 refers to magazine capacity: hence the P7M13 carries the 13 rounds specified by the US pistol tests. The M8 carries eight rounds, making for a more concealable gun.

9-mm Parabellum
The gas retarded mechanism is sensitive to pressure curve variations and only really likes full-power factory ammunition. If you are bold enough to hand-load 9-mm rounds, restrict yourself to fast-burning powders and eschew lighter bullets.

Piston
This can only retract when the round has left the barrel and pressure has fallen to a safe level. This then makes the slide recoil and eject the spent case. On the way back it chambers the next round.

Squeeze cocking lever
Unless this is pushed in the trigger cannot be released, so accidental firing is a little harder. It needs about 15-lb pressure to cock the striker but only about 2 lb to hold it cocked.

Below: The Bushman is a new design that points a possible way forward for the military pistol. It is a complete weapon system that can be a pistol or an SMG with a stock.

Right: Iranian women of the Civil Militia take aim with a collection of early Beretta Model 92s and a Browning High Power. The variety of grips and the shooting stances underline the major problem of the military pistol: you have to know what you are doing to hit anything. New designs try to compensate for a lack of training by enhancing natural balance and pointability and eliminating manual safeties.

Left: The Colt 1911A served the US Army well for many decades before it started to show its age. It was replaced by the Beretta 92 – a lighter weapon with almost double the magazine capacity. The pistol trials that produced this result were very acrimonious.

Right: Officially chosen as the replacement for the Colt was the Beretta Model 92. Designs from both Colt and Smith & Wesson were rejected during the replacement trials, and S&W even launched legal action. However, the Beretta remains an excellent choice.

TUNNEL RATS

The US were amazed to discover the huge warren of VC tunnels cutting through the hills of the jungle. It took a very special soldier to go in there and flush out the enemy.

Tunnels for hospitals, for hiding, for fighting – the American commanders arriving in Vietnam had never come across anything like them before. After initial bruising experiences, it became clear that they would need to develop a new military skill in tunnel warfare, and develop it fast.

US Army commanders were astonished by the scale and extent of the Viet Cong tunnel systems. Tunnel exploration and destruction was entirely ad hoc. There was no body of knowledge or experience upon which to draw. US soldiers improvised crawling and measuring techniques; some died underground by suffocation when smoke grenades had been used, others from Viet Cong booby traps and mines. A confidential

Left: Rats often found themselves emerging from the tunnels and staring into the barrel of an M16, then trying to persuade its owner that they were American.

EYE WITNESS

Tunnel fighting

"I felt more fear than I've ever come close to before or since. The Viet Cong would take their dead after a battle and put them down in the tunnels; they didn't want us to count their dead because they knew we were big on body count. Finding them wasn't pleasant, but we'd killed them so it didn't matter. It was worse if they'd been down there for a week – it stunk! Everything rotted very quickly because of the humidity. I came across rotting bodies several times. It didn't revolt me. I was just an animal – we were all animals, we were dogs, we were snakes, we were dirt. We weren't human beings – human beings don't do the things we did."

Sergeant Harold Roper, 25th Infantry Division, Vietnam, 1966

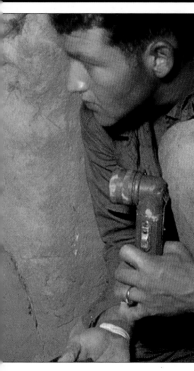

Above: In the pitch black of the tunnels the torch was of life-saving importance. You had to carry it away from your body to avoid it becoming a target.

Above: Webbing and kit was not for the tunnel rat. He was a soldier stripped to the very barest necessities – a gun and a torch.

report, *Operations Against Tunnel Complexes,* listed the inherent dangers of underground exploration. As well as citing bad air and booby traps, it included somewhat superfluously, "VC still in the tunnel." But its main recommendation was the creation of a specialist soldier, a new military skill unique to the Vietnam War. The creation of those teams would prove one of the more extraordinary phenomena in the history of American arms: the birth of an infantryman who rejoiced in the undignified but menacing title of 'Tunnel Rat'.

Temperament and courage

This task demanded not only special skills, but – it was recognised – a special type of temperament and courage. The tunnel rats were obliged to perform the most unnatural and stressful of tasks: to crawl through pitch-dark, narrow, low earthen tunnels for hundreds of yards, facing the threat of sudden death at any moment. Heavily armed Viet Cong units hid in their underground refuges for most of the daylight hours. In addition,

every tunnel was sown with mines and booby traps. There were fire ants, rats (real ones), and other creatures. In damp black holes dug for the slim and slight Vietnamese, most Americans found claustrophobia panic barely controllable.

"It's amazing what human beings will do in that sort of situation," said Captain Herbert Thornton, one of the first of the new tunnel rats.

"It just takes a special kind of being. He's got to have an inquisitive mind, a lot of guts, and a lot of real moxie into knowing what to touch and what not to touch to stay alive. Because you could blow yourself out of there in a heartbeat if you didn't really keep your eyes open all the time. There were no bad days. They were all good days if you got through them."

Why did Thornton think tunnel specialists were needed? "At first

we tried to put tunnel teams all over the division, and we had people getting zapped because they didn't have enough knowledge." There were horrible and bizarre ways to die under the ground; one Viet Cong technique was to slit a man's throat or garotte him as he came up through a connecting trapdoor. None of his chemical platoon, he claimed, was zapped in the one year he spent on that assignment.

Marked man

The efficient Viet Cong intelligence-gathering soon knew of Captain Thornton's special tunnel duties; despite his junior rank, he was a marked man. Reward notices were posted by the Communists, calling for Thornton's death; there was a price on the tunnel specialist's head. He survived, however, to become the tunnel guru.

In the years that followed,

esprit among tunnel rats increased to the point that they had a special cloth badge made and an (unofficial) sleeve insignia. The badge showed a grey rodent holding a pistol and flashlight, and had a motto in dog Latin, *"Non Gratum Anus Rodentum"* – "Not worth a rat's ass."

The tunnel rat was to stand proud and isolated within the ranks of the best-equipped army in the world. Not for him the standard infantryman's equipment of steel helmet, full combat dress, flak jacket, lightweight jungle boots, full webbing, water bottle, M1 or M16 automatic rifle, and spare ammunition bandolier. To the contrary, the tunnel rat soon discovered that lack of equipment was an advantage – the less he took into the sweaty darkness the better his chances of survival. The more they tried to arm him, the more he was to realise that neither firepower, personal armour, nor new-fangled high technology, would ever give him an advantage over his invisible enemy.

As tunnel rat volunteers began to step forward, experience soon showed that the knife, the pistol, and the flashlight were to be the basic tools for combat and survival inside the tunnels of Cu Chi. Indeed, the very reverse of high-tech weapons development took place within the tiny ranks of the tunnel rats. They had to relearn the whole business of carefully planned face-to-face combat, one-on-one as they called it, without fire support, and without weapons superiority.

Unarmed combat

The rats were to become obsessive about the most minute detail of their equipment, lauding the virtues of one pistol over another, one knife edge over another. They rediscovered the satisfaction of old-fashioned unarmed combat, where individual strength, guts, and cunning counted for much more than

massive air and artillery support.

Every rat carried a flashlight, and carried it in a special way to avoid being a nicely lit target. If the flashlight were dropped and the bulb smashed, then panic could easily follow, so they learned how to change a bulb in pitch darkness by touch alone, and they learned how to do it quickly, and how to do it squatting, kneeling, or lying prone.

Colt .45

The only weapon the tunnel rats ever agreed about was the Army's standard-issue Colt .45. No one wanted it, and very few used it. It was too big, too cumbersome, and too loud. Choosing your own pistol was a tunnel rat privilege and each sought the weapon he felt comfortable with.

They disagreed about silencers. Some would not fire a pistol without because of the deafening roar of the shot, others wouldn't fire one with because the added barrel length made it too awkward for a quick-draw or for manoeuvrability within the tiny claustrophobic tunnel confines – indeed, sometimes they deliberately wished to advertise their presence in order to frighten the VC out of the tunnel. Not many tunnel rats actively sought and welcomed tunnel combat, surely one of the most terrifying encounters imaginable.

PFC Harold Roper simply bought a .38 Smith & Wesson from a helicopter pilot for $25 and used that, together with a shotgun, where appropriate. The large pellet scatter of the shotgun made it potentially a more accurate tunnel weapon, although

not necessarily as lethal as a pistol. Master Sergeant Flo Rivera appropriated his own German Luger and managed to arrange official issue of a four-gauge riot shotgun – "really handy that four-gauge, the noise blew your eardrums out but if there was anything at all in front of you, you hit it."

Major Randy Ellis, who led one of the tunnel rat squads, also favoured an unsilenced Smith & Wesson .38, but was worried about its lack of firepower in the face of the VC's AK-47. So he acquired an M-2 carbine with a "paratrooper" stock, which folded up to about 22 inches in length. The weapon was nicknamed "The Cannon", and if Ellis led a tunnel rat squad down a hole, the number three rat always carried it. If the point man (lead man) then suspected there was a VC ahead, he would call for the cannon. Sergeant Bernard Justen rejected a specially silenced .38 with a unique light-source sniper-scope in favour of his own simple .25 Beretta.

Smell the enemy

Ultimately, the tunnel rat's best piece of equipment was a body tuned to near perfection, where every part was guaranteed. The successful rat had to volunteer to go down and stay down and take risks that were unmatched by anything he would ever meet above ground. Even if he were small by American standards, he had to negotiate bends in the communications tunnels that would only just let a slim Vietnamese through. He had to conquer an instinctive tendency to hyperventilate and remember that

Above: For the men who volunteered to join the rats, life in the tunnels became an obsession. The more sub-human the tasks they had to perform, the more they wanted to get back in there.

Right: It was rare to find a black tunnel rat; they tended to be too large. The job usually fell to the wiry Latin Americans or the smaller whites. It was a war where the scrawny were often the best.

victory could only be achieved once he had come to terms with his own fear. His fingertips and ears became like a walking stick to a blind man. After a while, he could "smell" the enemy ahead, not just through odour but sensing him like a bat, that other creature of darkness which employs primitive sonar to avoid or detect at night.

SHOOT TO LIVE!

You can be the best shot in the world, able to hit a tin can at a hundred paces, but you must also be able to survive on the battlefield.

Pistols have short barrels with a short sight radius – a short distance between the foresight and the rear sight. They are at their best when fired with two hands, not one-handed like American TV cops. In combat they will be fired under the stress of having the enemy at very close quarters.

These combined factors make the pistol a very difficult weapon to shoot well. Most people cannot hit a barn door at 15 metres. So unlike a rifle, which has a natural accuracy because of its long barrel and stability, a pistol is inherently inaccurate: you need to put a lot of rounds downrange to become proficient.

Having said that, you can learn to be the best pistol target shot in the world but if you don't know anything about tactics you will not survive.

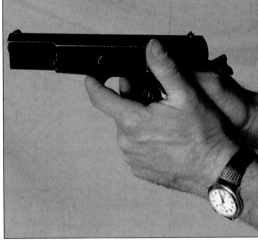

Conditioned response

Under conditions of great stress, such as when someone is trying to kill you, you revert to a complete non-intellectual condition known as conditioned response. You do not make decisions in the normal way but as an automatic reaction. Your brain cannot cope with the speed of the situation.

The key to survival under such conditions is to train your body to respond automatically to a wide range of threats, practising the same drills again and again until it becomes second nature. This is very important in a pistol gunfight, where engagements are so short: the annual US FBI crime report indicates that the average handgun fight lasts 2.8 seconds, with a total expenditure of 2.7 rounds of ammo. It takes place in dim light at an average range of just seven feet! Seventy-five per cent of all pistol fights are at a range of under seven yards. If it happens, it happens fast and at very close range.

Correct grip

Do not shoot one-handed. You should hold a pistol by jamming it between your controlling and supporting hands; the former is the hand you use to pull the trigger. Keep your finger and thumbs clear of the slide, as this may cause a stoppage if you accidently foul its path. Push out with your controlling hand and pull back with your supporting hand. The two recognised grips are the Weaver grip, where the forefinger of the supporting hand curls round the trigger guard, and the Cooper grip, where the supporting hand is underneath the guard.

The Weaver grip (above right) has the forefinger of the supporting hand around the trigger guard. The Cooper grip is shown right. They both provide a stable handhold; the choice between them is largely a matter of personal preference.

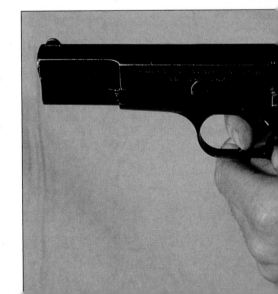

SHOOT TO LIVE!

Left: For Special Forces, the pistol is an ideal weapon. It packs a large punch in a small package. Always be aware of inherent danger; the gun should be drawn at all times and ready to fire immediately.

Movement

Remember these rules:

1 Never leave your pistol in its holster when you are under threat. All this speed-draw stuff is for cowboys. Keep a good, stable position, with the pistol just below your line of sight.
2 Never run unless you are actually being shot at.
3 Move by shuffling in the ready position, and do not cross your feet.
4 Keep your balance at all times!
5 Do not lie down unless you have to.

Load procedure

Most auto pistols use a box magazine fitted in the pistol's grip. To load, insert the magazine in the magazine well, and drive it home. There is no need to give it an extra thwack; just check that it is fully home by pulling back on it. The weapon can be carried safely in this condition.

Making ready

To cock the weapon, pinch in on the slide with your forefinger and thumb. Make sure your trigger finger is outside the trigger guard. Pull the slide back and release it, allowing it to run forward. This picks up the first round and loads it into the chamber. The weapon is then ready to fire.

Left: All that barrel-in-the-small-of-the-back stuff went out with calling your boss 'Kimo Sabe'. Maximise the distance between you and your attacker.

Above: Most pistols are designed for simple and fast reloading. By using your forefinger as a guide you will not have to fumble around trying to find the magazine well.

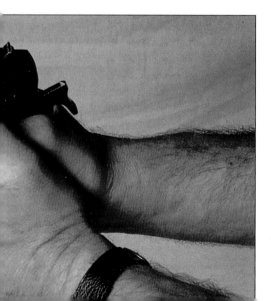

Below: The foresight alone allows a reasonably accurate shot to be taken. If there is time, line up your target, the foresight and the rearsight for maximum accuracy.

The six rules of common sense

1 Use your eyes and ears! You have to be aware of all the fine detail going on around you. Normally you bimble along completely unaware of the world around you, your brain seeing things selectively and filling in the rest of the information using things that it considers to be normal. You must use all your senses to analyse the potential danger in every situation.

2 Never turn your back on anything you have not already checked out. Never put your back towards a cupboard in a house or an uncleared room. Look up in the trees as well as down on the ground.

3 Stay away from corners: they are death traps. Move out and away from them to give you more time should there be someone waiting round the corner.

4 Always maximise the distance between you and a potential attacker. The closer you are, the easier it is for him to get you and you have less time to react. You may think a soldier across the room from you armed with a knife is no problem if you are armed with a pistol, but there are plenty of cases of soldiers and policemen being killed before they have had time to even draw their gun.

5 Never lose your balance: this includes not running unless you are actually under fire. Stay in a solid, ready position, and move at a brisk pace. Slow down to a shuffle in the places where you think you may have to fire a shot.

6 Concentrate on the foresight. At close range there will be no time to take proper aim. Concentrate on the foresight and you will almost certainly hit the target.

Far left and left: The difference between single-action and double-action motion. The right-hand picture shows the gun manually cocked; squeezing the trigger will cause the hammer to fall. This is single action. The gun in the far left picture is double action. Pulling the trigger will cause the hammer to be cocked (1st action) and then fall (2nd action).

Trigger operation

Good trigger release is essential for control and accuracy. For single-action pistols, the pad of your forefinger contacts the trigger and immediately takes up the slack when a target is acquired. While controlling your breathing and maintaining the correct sight picture, you slowly increase the pressure on the trigger until the hammer is released and fires the round. This is known as a surprise brake, as you do not know exactly when the hammer will fall. This technique is used during combat shooting, but the time taken to squeeze is compressed: this is known as the compressed surprise brake trigger squeeze. You must master this technique in order to become an accurate combat shot.

The double tap

Take a correct sight picture for the first shot. Release the shot and follow through, and as soon as the weapon recovers from recoil, fire another round immediately without looking through the sights again. With practice you will be able to fire two shots virtually together, which hit within a few centimetres of each other.

Speed reload

Never fire so that your chamber is left empty. Count your rounds and leave one in the chamber while you reload. Beware the Browning High Power, which has a magazine safety that prevents you firing the weapon without a mag. To speed reload, eject the empty magazine and reach for the next mag. Hold it with the forefinger of your hand down the leading edge of the magazine. Tip the pistol on its side. Insert the mag in the magazine well, and drive it home.

Two rounds fired quickly at the same target is known as a double tap. Some pistols are a bit short on stopping power: double the rounds does double the damage.

Firing positions

There are no short cuts to becoming a good combat pistol shot. You need speed, accuracy and tactics: it is no good being fast if you can't hit anything. First, you need to master the basic shooting positions that make your body a stable weapons platform.

1 Isosceles stance

This offers reasonable speed with a fair degree of accuracy. It is popular with police units as it is easy to teach. Face the target with a shoulders' width between your feet. Hold your controlling and supporting arm straight out and adopt the correct grip position. You may prefer to sit down further into the position.

2 Weaver stance

This position is the fastest; it offers accuracy with excellent control of the pistol. Stand at 45 degrees to the target with an average pace between your feet. Shoot across your body with your left shoulder facing the target. The pistol is sandwiched between your controlling hand pushing away from your body and your supporting hand pulling back.

3 The combat crouch

At very close range the combat crouch is faster. Punch both hands towards the target, focusing the foresight on the centre of the target's body mass. Throw your right leg back and crouch to make yourself less of a target.

The Isosceles stance is easy to teach recruits and is quick to adopt. It is popular with bodyguards and police since it is easy to switch directions to face a new threat, but it does present your entire upper body to the enemy as a target.

The Weaver stance is the position preferred by the FBI and US police. It is a very accurate position and provides a stable platform for the firer. Also, by adopting a stance at 45 degrees to the target, the size of target you present to the enemy is reduced.

The combat crouch is the quickest and perhaps most natural stance to adopt. This is real last-minute, whites-of-the-eyes time. If you miss at this range you won't have to worry about the niceties of other stances and positions.

COMBAT REVOLVERS

Few military units are now equipped with revolvers, but their rugged reliability makes them favourite weapons with police and paramilitary forces worldwide.

From his black ski mask to his $150 hi-top tennis shoes, the man stood well over six feet tall. The twin muzzles of his shotgun swept around the liquor store like a security camera. Two would-be customers stood stock still, staring at the rain outside and trying to avoid the gunman's gaze. With trembling hands, the owner dumped handfuls of dollar bills into a bag on the counter. The gunman's muscled arm seized it and, with a menacing flourish of his shotgun, he headed for the door.

He heard the challenge, but his car was waiting, engine running. He swung the gun around, but not fast enough. Officer Wilson had been retired for some years now, but his Colt Python was still in business. Two 125-grain .357 Magnum rounds slammed into the gunman, toppling him to the ground and terminating the proceedings. 'God created men,' the saying goes, 'and Colonel Colt made them equal.'

Colt's great equaliser is now over 150 years old; he was granted his first patent in 1836. Modern revolvers can fire much more deadly ammunition and are surprisingly accurate in experienced hands. The renowned American pistol shooter Elmer Keith once hit and killed

A US police officer from a SWAT unit rushes a child to safety as his colleagues storm a building where a man was holding several people hostage.

The Professional's View:

The revolver

"The revolver has been a primary weapon for law enforcement for over a century. Different calibres and different loads continue to be offered as the 'ultimate' solution to stopping a felon in the fastest time possible. Yet it is important to remember than even the most effective loads like the Federal .357 Magnum 125-grain jacketed hollow point cannot guarantee an immediate result. They represent the best compromise between cartridge load and controllability. Any revolver is ultimately limited by its size. No real revolver can hurl its target across a room like they do in the movies."

Lieutenant S. Benedetto, Cook County Police Department

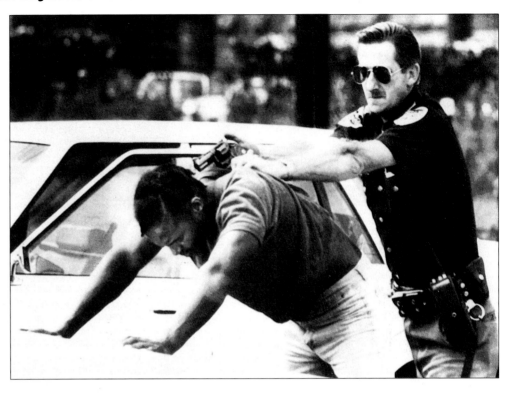

A US police officer arrests a man after a bank robbery in Indianapolis. The revolver is a 4-inch barrel Colt Python .357 Magnum. Introduced in 1955, the Python today costs around $800 but its high standards of manufacture and fine shooting qualities have enabled it to remain popular well into its fourth decade.

a mule deer at 600 yards using his .44 Magnum. But he was an exception who set a standard most other shooters can only aspire to. The practical range of a typical modern revolver is 50 yards at best. Comparisons between pistols can be misleading – while some are undoubtedly more accurate than others, the difference will only show if the guns are fired from a bench rest. In a gunfight, good pistol handling counts for much more than minute technical advantages.

Revolvers had been in widespread use for several generations before the first handguns sprayed smoke and flame in front of the movie cameras. They have remained a favourite prop in films ever since. As a result, more myths surround the revolver than perhaps any other weapon. What they can, and cannot, do may come as a surprise to the movie-goer inexperienced in handling firearms.

Revolvers are close-range weapons; James Cagney's parting shot in *White Heat*, or almost any western, shows them hitting targets at great distances with no trouble taken to aim them. Clint Eastwood's revolvers lift his enemies clean off their feet and usually kill them stone dead. In reality, not even a hit

from a high-powered rifle can achieve this. It may well kill, but it will not fling a human target through a window like a rag doll. Even the most powerful handgun cartridges will only score an instant knock-down if they strike the head, spinal column or fracture a leg.

This does not mean that revolvers are ineffective weapons. The right revolver with the right ammunition can certainly sledge down the most drug-filled crazie. With fewer parts to go wrong, they inspire more confidence than most automatic pistols and remain the standard police handgun in many law enforcement agencies worldwide.

The revolver's major weakness as a military weapon is its six-shot cylinder. Since the introduction of the Browning High-Power and

other 9-mm pistols which can pack more than twice as many rounds into their magazines, the revolver has been outmatched. With criminals in the USA employing modern 9-mm weapons with 18-shot magazines, an increasing number of police departments are selecting the latest automatics instead. They have the added advantage that if an inexperienced attacker seizes an officer's firearm, he may not be able to use it immediately. The time while he fumbles with the safety catches and slide releases may save that officer's life.

The introduction of speed-loading devices has reduced the revolver's principal disadvantage. Traditionally-minded authorities preferred officers to load from old-style cartridge loops, but speed-loaders are now

COMBAT REVOLVERS Reference File

249

USA

Smith & Wesson .357 Magnum

Smith & Wesson manufactures several revolvers capable of firing the powerful .357 Magnum round. The most popular are its two medium-frame .357s, the Model 586 and Model 686. The former is blued, the latter stainless steel, and both are offered in a variety of barrel lengths. These range from the 2½-in barrel intended for concealed carry to the 8⅜-in hunting/target shooting model. For police and security use, 4- or 6-in barrels are the norm.

Unlike some earlier .357s, the 586/686 series is designed to survive an unvaried diet of full-power Magnum ammunition without rattling to bits. Lighter-built weapons really intended to spend their lives firing .38 +P loads proved incapable of sustained service

firing Magnum cartridges. Apart from sheer strength of construction, the S&W 586/686 range offers a number of advantages. Its cylinder release catch is very fast to open, and the target grips are cut away at the top to allow unrestricted access with a speed-loader. Trigger pull can obviously be adjusted and rubber or neoprene grips added, but for an out-of-the-box revolver the S&Ws are hard to beat.

Specification
Smith & Wesson Model 686
Calibre: .357 Magnum
Length: up to 290 mm (12 in)
Weight: 1.4 kg
Barrel lengths: 63.5, 101.6, 152.4 or 212.7 mm (2½, 4, 6 or 8⅜ in)

Cylinder capacity: six shots
Finish: matt stainless steel or (Model 586) blued or (1989 limited edition only) midnight black

A limited-edition midnight black 3-inch barrel Smith & Wesson Model 686 shown with semi-jacketed hollow-point bullets.

Bullet types

1 Lead round nose
Usually used for target shooting, where rapid loading is necessary.

2 Lead semi wad cutter SWC
Gives a very clean cut edge on a paper target, which facilitates scoring.

3 Lead hollow point
This round has some hunting application, but can disintegrate rather than mushroom.

4 Wad cutter
A lead target bullet which leaves a clean print on paper targets. All lead bullets tend to leave more fouling in the barrel than FMJ.

5 Full metal jacket
All military pistol ammunition is of this format. Not usually used for target work.

6 Semi-jacketed hollow point
Primarily a hunting bullet, it expands rapidly on striking the target with the sides peeling back round the jacket.

7 Pointed soft point
This is a hunting round which is more likely to function in automatics.

8 Semi-jacketed soft point
A very effective hunting round that is far more ballistically efficient than full metal jacket.

9 Hollow base wad cutter
A target shooting bullet that is difficult to speed load.

Revolvers remain popular as police/security weapons because of their proven reliability. Compared with an automatic pistol, there is very little to go wrong. The officer here employs the Isosceles stance: standing square onto the target. Two-handed shooting is preferred for its much greater accuracy, although officers must be able to shoot left- and right-handed as the situation demands.

standard. The most popular police revolver, in the UK as well as the USA, is the Smith and Wesson Model 66. It fires .38-inch calibre bullets which are manufactured in a wide variety of styles.

Unfortunately, the British police continue to rely on the widely discredited 158-grain round-nose bullet. Extensive experience in the USA has shown this ammunition to be dangerous to the public and the police. It can certainly inflict lethal injury, but criminals shot with it have been known to continue to kill people *after* they have suffered fatal wounds. If a criminal's actions have forced authorities to employ lethal force, the lethality must be as instantaneous as possible.

More effective .38-calibre ammunition is available. Perhaps the most effective is the so-called 'Chicago load' – a 158-grain lead hollow point which mushrooms effectively on impact. Incidentally, the Geneva Convention, which bans expanding or explosive bullets, only applies to military ammunition; it specifically excludes law enforcement. However, most forces have now re-equipped with .357 Magnums.

Magnum ammunition was first developed for hunting animals. Introduced in 1935, the .357 is based on a lengthened and strengthened .38-calibre case. The extra length also performs a valuable safety function, making this very powerful round too long to fit in the cylinder of a standard .38-calibre revolver. The Magnum has become a household name, again thanks to Hollywood, but its police value depends very much on choosing the appropriate Magnum round.

Most Magnums are simply too powerful for safe use in law enforcement. Passing clean through the target, they exit with sufficient velocity to penetrate walls and kill innocent bystanders. The introduction of hollow points by the Super Vel Cartridge Corporation during the 1960s led to a series of .357 hollow-point rounds being offered. Unfortunately, the lightweight and incredibly fast 110-grain

250

USA

Smith & Wesson .44 Magnum

Smith & Wesson introduced the .44 Magnum cartridge in 1956 for its Model 29 revolver. It was developed to meet the demand for something more powerful than the .357 Magnum. S&W certainly succeeded: the .44 develops over twice the muzzle energy of the .357. Still, it remained a relatively obscure calibre until Clint Eastwood wielded one with such deadly efficiency in the movie *Dirty Harry*. Sales soared, and Smith & Wesson never really looked back.

The .44 Magnum was originally designed for handgun hunting – it is suitable for most game animals up to and including deer. But the cachet of 'the most powerful handgun in the world' proved irresistible for many

individuals and police officers. Unfortunately, it demands considerable practice to shoot well with the full-power .44 Magnum. Obviously the shooter can download his ammunition, but that negates the whole point of buying the Model 29 in the first place. The ammunition is certainly capable of target shooting accuracy, but only a few shooters can manage it.

Smith & Wesson's full range now includes the Model 629, the stainless steel version of the original blued Model 29. During 1988 it manufactured 5,000 of the limited edition 'Classic Hunters', a heavy-barrelled .44 Magnum with an unfluted cylinder. This is an outstanding handgun already much sought-after.

Smith & Wesson scored a major success with the .44 Magnum. Ruger and now Colt have followed suit with .44s of their own.

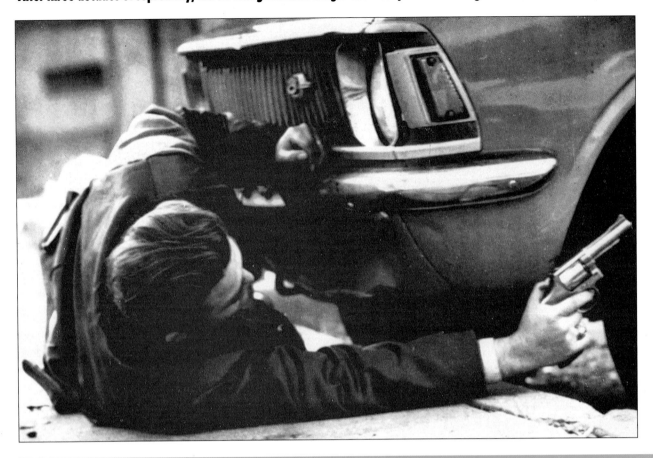

A police officer was involved in a shoot-out in New Orleans which ended in the death of one suspect and the arrest of another after an armed robbery. The engine block is one of the few parts of a car that offers any protection from large-calibre handgun ammunition.

251

USA

Ruger GP100 .357 Magnum

Ruger firearms have established a reputation for innovative design, and the GP100 revolver sets new standards for strength and safety. The sidewalls are solid, with the lock mechanism and trigger guard as a single sub-assembly. The cylinder latch is offset to the right, enabling the stop notches to be cut between the chambers instead of directly over them. This substantially increases the strength of the cylinder.

The cylinder is locked into the frame in two places, the usual cylinder pin at the rear being supplemented by a spring-loaded latch at the front of the crane. This arrangement was invented by Ruger to ensure that the cylinder and barrel are correctly aligned. The GP100 also introduced the cushioned

grips which make Ruger revolvers so instantly recognisable. The one-piece Monsanto Santoprene grips combine live rubber with walnut or high-impact resin inserts. They are expressly designed to reduce the discomfort caused by the recoil forces of .357 Magnum loads.

Unlike S&W revolvers, Rugers employ a floating firing pin mounted in the frame. The hammer strikes a transfer bar that will not impinge on the firing pin unless the trigger is being pulled. Until then it stays retracted, out of the hammer's way, so the gun will not fire unless the trigger is pulled.

It took little time for the GP100 to be recognized as a high-quality security revolver. It is used by police in the USA.

Specification
Ruger GP100
Calibre: .357 Magnum
Length: up to 288.9 mm (11⅜ in)
Weight: 1.1-1.3 kg, depending on

model
Barrel length: 76.2, 101.6 or 152.4 mm (3, 4 or 6 in)
Cylinder capacity: six shots
Finish: blued or stainless steel

252

USA

Ruger Redhawk .44 Magnum

The Redhawk and Super Redhawk provide S&W's greatest competition in the .44 Magnum market. Like the GP100, they employ a floating firing pin and are built for maximum strength. The barrel is forged with integral rib and ejector housing, while the frame has no sideplates to weaken the sidewalls. The cylinder is locked in place by the same system as that on the GP100 and the trigger action is good without any adjustment. Using Ruger's patented single-spring mechanism, the trigger and hammer are powered by opposite ends of the same massive coil spring.

Offered with a 5½- or 7½-in barrel, the Redhawk is intended for game or silhouette shooting. But for longer-range metallic silhouette or target

shooting, Ruger has introduced the Super Redhawk. These guns have massive extended frames with thick top straps fitted for the Ruger Integral Scope Mounted System, and are sold with stainless steel scope rings as standard. Their 7½- or 9½-in barrels have a ramp front sight base to use the interchangeable notch blades provided for the Redhawk. Redhawks are currently provided with wooden grips, and the Super Redhawks use the rubber-wrapped versions, as fitted to the GP100.

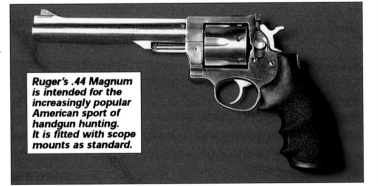

Ruger's .44 Magnum is intended for the increasingly popular American sport of handgun hunting. It is fitted with scope mounts as standard.

Specification
Super Redhawk
Calibre: .44 Magnum
Length: 330.2 mm (13 in) or 381 mm

(15 in)
Weight: 1.5 or 1.65 kg, depending on barrel length
Barrel length: 190.5 or 241.3 mm (7½ or 9½ in)

Cylinder capacity: six shots
Finish: brush satin stainless steel

The famous American fighter pilot Colonel Robin Olds pre-flights his F-4 Phantom with a revolver strapped to his hip and cartridge loops full of ammunition. Revolvers were carried by aircrew from 1914 through to the Vietnam War.

bullets tended to disintegrate against car windscreens or other cover. The tougher 158-grain versions travelled so fast that they continued to pass through the felon without expanding.

Remington produced a 125-grain semi-jacketed hollow-point .357 Magnum in the mid-1970s and this has proved to be the most effective round available. With a muzzle velocity of some 1,200 feet per second, the bullet soon showed itself able to slam into the target and stay there, delivering all its energy where it counts. Its stopping power exceeds that of any other revolver round – even the .44 Magnum, which usually motors clean through the target and continues on its way at high speed.

Revolvers chambered for Magnum cartridges have one major problem. The fierce recoil makes them hard to control. Wooden chequered grips have to be replaced by rub-

---

253

 USA

Colt .357 Magnum

Introduced in 1955, Colt's .357 Python remains highly regarded and still commands a hefty price tag. Because it is so much more expensive than the competition, Colt introduced a 'budget' version, the King Cobra. The latter is easily distinguished because it lacks the Python's distinctive ventilated rib, and it is a common choice in US law enforcement. The Python's double action is outstanding, and for fast, accurate shooting it has few rivals. The high cost results from the guns being built individually and assembled by hand. Combining the strength and reliability of a combat weapon with the accuracy of a custom-made target revolver, the Python has been widely imitated but not surpassed.

The full-length ejector rod housing helps to balance the revolver for rapid double-action shooting. The cylinder notches are offset to increase the strength of the cylinder, and red ramp sights are supplied as standard. Unlike Smith & Wessons and Rugers, the cylinder on a Colt revolves clockwise. The Colt's only disadvantage is the cylinder release catch, which has to be pulled backwards to release. This is fractionally slower than the Ruger or S&W systems.

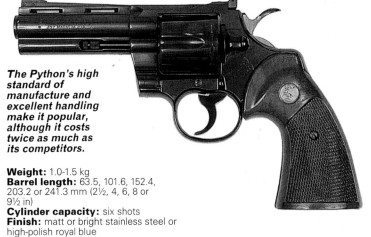

The Python's high standard of manufacture and excellent handling make it popular, although it costs twice as much as its competitors.

Specification
Colt Python
Calibre: .357 Magnum
Length: 203.2-342.9 mm (8-13½ in), depending on barrel length

Weight: 1.0-1.5 kg
Barrel length: 63.5, 101.6, 152.4, 203.2 or 241.3 mm (2½, 4, 6, 8 or 9½ in)
Cylinder capacity: six shots
Finish: matt or bright stainless steel or high-polish royal blue

---

254

SPAIN

Llama Comanche

The Spanish firm of Llama is one of several European companies to manufacture American-style revolvers. Combining the ventilated rib of the Colt Python with an S&W-type cylinder and cylinder release catch, they have a substantial price advantage over their US counterparts. The Comanche's hammer pivots on a cam which prevents accidental firing if the gun were dropped and landed on the hammer. The frame is forged in high-grade steel, and the ejector rod housing extends almost to the end of the barrel. The wooden grips are cut away on the left-hand side to allow easier access with a speed-loader.

Unfortunately, Llama revolvers cannot match the quality of the three

leading US pistol manufacturers. The frame of the Comanche is fabricated from high-grade steel, but other parts are not hardened. This limits their life to about three years of hard use because the hammers tend to give light strikes as they wear down. Llamas are certainly a cost-effective starting point for full-bore shooting, but they will not outlast a Ruger, an S&W or a Colt.

Specification
Llama Comanche
Calibre: .357 Magnum
Length: 290 mm (12 in)
Weight: 1.3 kg
Barrel length: 152.4 mm (6 in)
Cylinder capacity: six shots
Finish: blued

The Llama Comanche is one of several American-style .357 Magnums produced in Europe. Few European revolvers match the quality of the leading US products.

Several handguns were tested against a car: the door failed to stop any major-calibre ammunition. Note the rubber grips added to the .44 Magnum; these are important in soaking up the ferocious recoil from this very powerful cartridge.

ber or neoprene to cushion the blow. The shock tends to make the shooter flinch as he or she anticipates the blow, which reduces the accuracy of the shot. Since a weapon's lethality only becomes relevant if you can hit the target, the Magnum is only worth issuing to personnel well-trained in firing it.

In the last 20 years revolvers have become widely used for sport in the USA. The same powerful Magnums used for law enforcement are often used to fire .38 bullets – the heavier-framed weapons reducing recoil and increasing accuracy in competition shooting. Before laws made most handguns illegal in the UK, 50,000+ handguns in Britain were revolvers. These were outnumbered by some 300,000 illegally held weapons confiscated over the last 50 years, which include vast numbers of wartime Webley revolvers that former servicemen kept in their lofts. loft.

Because they are so much simpler to use than automatics, revolvers remain the prime choice of privately-owned handgun in the USA. The popularity of handgun hunting and the multitude of target shooting disciplines have led manufacturers to develop special-purpose weapons. With rape and murder seldom out of the newspaper headlines, revolvers also continue to act as a great leveller. At a recent rally in the USA, a young woman's T-shirt sported the legend: 'God created men and women equal. Smith & Wesson keeps it that way.'

Keeping men and women equal: short-barrelled .38 revolvers are the most popular choice for a self-defence weapon in the USA. Smith & Wesson has just introduced the 'Lady Smith' expressly tailored to suit a woman's hand.

Developmen of the Revolver

The earliest revolvers were loaded with loose charges of black powder and a lead ball rammed down on top. The development of metal cartridge cases vastly improved their capability, and with the arrival of smokeless powder in the 1890s their reliability became excellent.

1851

Adams 38-bore .50-calibre revolver

Left: While Colt's revolvers were in full-scale factory production during the 1850s, British gunmakers like Adams sold a fine range of hand-crafted revolvers which were carried by military officers all over the world.

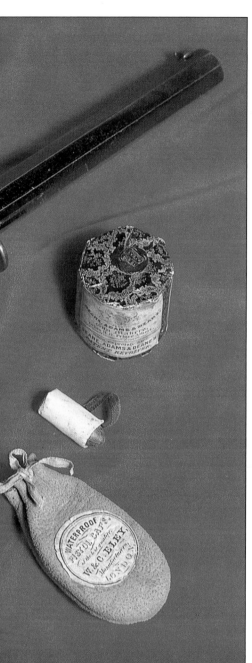

1895

Nagant 7.62-mm revolver

Above: Used by the Russian army until 1945, the Nagant had an unusual gas-seal system to maximise muzzle velocity. This had little value, and made the double action very stiff indeed.

1913

Webley .455 revolver

Above: Solid and reliable Webley pistols were used by British and Empire forces during both world wars. The .455 cartridge was designed as a 'man-stopper'.

1989

Smith & Wesson Model 686 .357 Magnum

Left: During the last 30 years, US manufacturers have produced more revolvers than ever before. Available in all sorts of calibres to suit a wide variety of sporting disciplines as well as home defence and police use, revolvers might not have a front-line role anymore, but they have a great future.

'KICK LIKE A HORSE'

The revolvers carried by British officers in 1914 were tough, reliable guns which had proved themselves under combat conditions. But revolvers have continued to develop throughout the century, and since the 1960s new weapons have been appearing with bewildering speed.

Since revolvers became popular over 150 years ago, they have been manufactured in an incredible variety of shapes and sizes. Today, they can be small enough to fit unobtrusively in an ankle holster, or large enough to fire rounds as powerful as a hunting rifle. Revolvers were carried as sidearms by military officers from the 1850s onwards. They were widely used by private citizens for personal protection in both Europe and America. As police forces were developed, they also adopted revolvers, and manufacturers were soon producing guns for their use.

Many armies had decided to adopt automatic pistols instead of revolvers before 1914. Although

wartime shortages forced their re-introduction during World War I, only a few armies retained revolvers after 1918. The British and Soviet armies were the only forces to use them in large numbers during World War II.

Today revolvers are used in law enforcement and for personal defence, target shooting and hunting. They fire bullets ranging from the tiny .22 rimfire to the mighty .454 Casull. Prices range from under £50 for wartime weapons or cheap second-hand models to £2,000 and upwards for the finest customised revolvers. Some very specialised pistols have been developed, carefully engineered to triumph in specific competitions.

The interest in historic firearms is vigorous enough for several companies to manufacture fully functional replicas of US Civil War period revolvers.

Barrel lengths are similarly modified to suit every taste. For concealed carry, two-inch barrelled 'snub' revolvers are ideal and new ones continue to appear on the market. For maximum concealment, the slim lines of a five-shot .38 are ideal. For maximum killing potential, cut-down .44 Magnums are also available, although the muzzle

blast is truly fearsome. The British police and most of their US counterparts rely on a four-inch barrel, six-inch barrels being too bulky for extended carry if the officer has to tote a large amount of other kit. At the other end of the scale, barrels of 10 inches or more are used for hunting and target shooting, especially metallic silhouette competitions. There is an appropriate revolver for almost any situation that demands the use of a handgun.

Pistol-packing Patton

George S. Patton was one of the most flamboyant generals of World War II. Rated by the Germans as the most dangerous Allied commander on the Western Front, his hard-driving tank formations spearheaded the Allied break-out from Normandy. He was frequently seen wearing two pearl-handled revolvers: a Smith & Wesson .357 Magnum and a Colt .45 single-action 1873 Army model. He had bought the .357 in 1935, the year in which it was first released. Although neither gun was fired in anger during World War II, the Colt had two notches in the handle from an encounter in 1916. During the US invasion of Mexico, launched to deal with Pancho Villa's guerrilla army, Patton led a patrol to the rancho San Miguelito. Inside was one of Villa's leading henchmen, Julio Cardenas, and several bodyguards. They charged out, only to find Patton standing in the gateway, pistol raised. He shot Cardenas dead and killed one of the bodyguards for good measure.

George S. Patton disembarks in North Africa during Operation Torch. He wore two revolvers throughout the war, and the two notches on the Colt .45 1873 Army commemorate his personal victory over two of Pancho Villa's Mexican guerrillas.

bullet into the rifling; condly, gas pressure is at the junction of the ing cone and the der. If this gap is too e, too much propellant pressure is lost, and if too small then the nder may become med by carbon residue ead shavings.

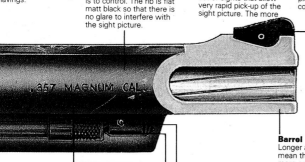

Top rib
This strengthens and adds weight to the barrel. The more weight there is forward, the easier recoil is to control. The rib is flat matt black so that there is no glare to interfere with the sight picture.

Front sight
Any firearm designed for use at close range and under pressure must have a good, clear, high-visibility set of sights that allow very rapid pick-up of the sight picture. The more

modern Rugers have detachable coloured inserts for the front sight to give a good sight picture under low light conditions.

Barrel
Longer and heavier barrels mean that the weapon is more accurate and tames the recoil of factory load .357 Magnum to an acceptable level so that recovery time between shots is minimised. Police pistols worn under the tunic in the UK are four-inch barrelled models as they are easier to conceal. In the US, police service revolvers are usually carried on the belt and so the six-inch barrel is usually favoured.

Front latch cross pin

Front latch
This engages the front of the ejector rod when the cylinder is closed.

Ejector rod
This is completely shrouded under the barrel. Some models, notably the Smith & Wesson Model 10 on issue to the British police, are exposed to damage. If you bend the ejection rod in any way you will end up having to poke the empty cases out individually with a pencil when you reload.

Cylinder centre pin rod

Ejector spring
After the ejector rod has been pressed to dump the empty cases in the cylinder, the spring returns the ejector to its closed position.

Cylinder centre pin spring

Cylinder latch spring

Cylinder latch
This prevents the cylinders moving at the moment of firing. It locks into the bottom of the cylinder, holding the chamber containing the round to be fired on line with the forcing cone.

Cylinder centre lock pin
This engages a cut-out in the frame to lock the cylinder closed.

Ejector
The ejector engages the rim of the cartridge cases to push them out. Revolvers can fire rimless cartridges but they are usually used with half moon clips where the ejector pushes against the clip.

Left: The Ruger Security Six .357 Magnum has now been replaced by the GP100 series double-action revolvers, but it illustrates several features that established Ruger's reputation for innovative revolver design. The top strap is very thick and the cylinder is locked not just at the rear but by an extra latch underneath at the front. Even with a round underneath the hammer, the gun will not fire if it falls to the ground and lands on the hammer. A transfer bar ensures that the revolver will only fire if the trigger is pulled.

Above: Unloading a Ruger GP100. The catch is pressed in, releasing the cylinder. Pushing upwards on the ejector rod expels the empty cases. The primers in the centre of each cartridge display a dent where they have been struck by the firing pin.

The self-cocking revolver

Patented in 1896 by Colonel G. V. Fosbery VC, the Webley-Fosbery automatic revolver was a compromise between the traditional revolver and an automatic action. The gun was cocked by thumbing back the hammer. The recoil drove the barrel and cylinder backwards along grooves in the frame. As the cylinder travelled back, a fixed stud in the frame engaged in the zig-zag channels around it, rotating it one-twelfth of a turn. Then the cylinder travelled forward again, revolving another twelfth of a turn, indexing a fresh cartridge under the hammer and re-cocking it. The Webley-Fosbery fired standard .455-inch pistol rounds and outshot the standard revolver in some competitions because it soaked up the recoil very well. Although never adopted by the British Army, it was used in the early part of World War I by officers who had purchased the gun privately. However, the mechanism proved insufficiently robust for field service, as mud and grit clogged the working parts.

The hybrid revolver/automatic Webley-Fosbery shot very accurately, and handicaps were introduced to keep some competitions fair before 1914. The idea was not unique: the Spanish Orbea revolver of 1863 was probably the first such hybrid, and Mauser also made one in limited numbers. The Webley-Fosbery was the only one of the type to see any real service.

Large-frame revolver

New designs and developments in metallurgy have allowed gun manufacturers to develop far more powerful revolvers than the weapons issued to armies at the turn of the century. Smith & Wesson were the pioneers in the 1930s with the introduction of the original .357 Magnum. The Colt Python of 1955 led to an 'arms race' between Colt, Smith & Wesson and Ruger, offering shooters an ever-increasing range of Magnum revolvers. By the mid-1970s, US police departments were training and doing their qualification shoots with full-power .357 Magnum loads. Since then, the market for Magnum-firing revolvers has continued to expand and gallons of ink have been expended in debating the best choice of .357 Magnum ammunition.

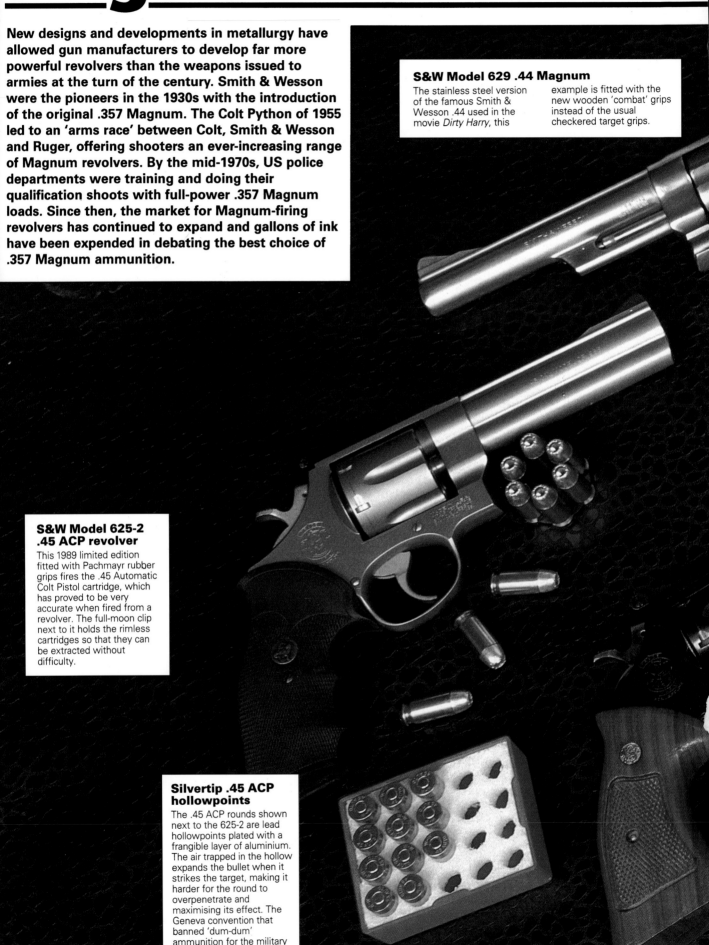

S&W Model 629 .44 Magnum
The stainless steel version of the famous Smith & Wesson .44 used in the movie *Dirty Harry*, this example is fitted with the new wooden 'combat' grips instead of the usual checkered target grips.

S&W Model 625-2 .45 ACP revolver
This 1989 limited edition fitted with Pachmayr rubber grips fires the .45 Automatic Colt Pistol cartridge, which has proved to be very accurate when fired from a revolver. The full-moon clip next to it holds the rimless cartridges so that they can be extracted without difficulty.

Silvertip .45 ACP hollowpoints
The .45 ACP rounds shown next to the 625-2 are lead hollowpoints plated with a frangible layer of aluminium. The air trapped in the hollow expands the bullet when it strikes the target, making it harder for the round to overpenetrate and maximising its effect. The Geneva convention that banned 'dum-dum' ammunition for the military specifically excluded law enforcement.

S&W Model 19 .357 Magnum

From the late 1950s to the mid-1970s, this was enormously popular with US police forces. Improved metallurgy allowed S&W to produce this .357 Magnum on the light and compact frame of the old .38 Special revolver. But when police forces began to use full Magnum loads, nearly treble the chamber pressure the 'K' frame was originally designed for, Model 19s were unable to take the strain.

S&W 1989 limited edition .357 Magnum

The unfluted cylinder offers extra strength and theoretically faster double action. Finished in satin stainless steel, it has a 6-inch barrel with the ejector shroud continued along the full length to help compensate for the recoil and bring the muzzle back on target more quickly.

S&W Model 28 'Highway Patrolman'

Just discontinued after 34 years in production, this was an economy version of the old Model 27 .357 Magnum. Offered with a 4- or 6-in barrel, it was an instant success and was one of the most popular heavy-duty revolvers carried by US police officers.

Colt Python .357 Magnum

With slightly faster rifling (one turn in 14-in rather than 18-in) and with a second cylinder hand to lock the cylinder firmly in place at the moment of firing, the Python has earned an excellent reputation for out-of-the-box accuracy. The barrel is fractionally smaller at the muzzle than at the forcing cone which forces the bullet into the rifling.

Inside the Ruger Security Six

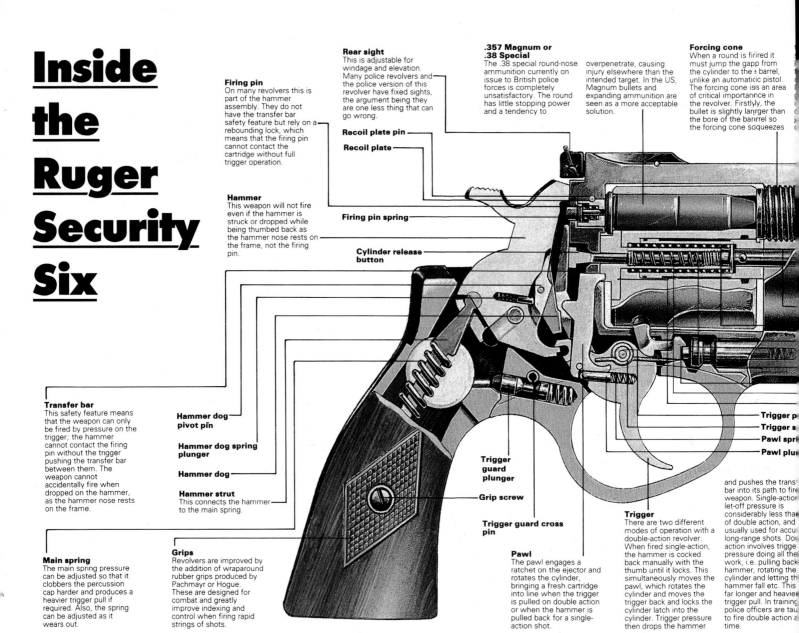

Firing pin
On many revolvers this is part of the hammer assembly. They do not have the transfer bar safety feature but rely on a rebounding lock, which means that the firing pin cannot contact the cartridge without full trigger operation.

Rear sight
This is adjustable for windage and elevation. Many police revolvers and the police version of this revolver have fixed sights, the argument being they are one less thing that can go wrong.

.357 Magnum or .38 Special
The .38 special round-nose ammunition currently on issue to British police forces is completely unsatisfactory. The round has little stopping power and a tendency to overpenetrate, causing injury elsewhere than the intended target. In the US, Magnum bullets and expanding ammunition are seen as a more acceptable solution.

Forcing cone
When a round is firired it must jump the gapp from the cylinder to the ꝛ barrel, unlike an automaticic pistol. The forcing cone iss an area of critical importance in the revolver. Firstlyly, the bullet is slightly larꝛrger than the bore of the barirrel so the forcing cone sꝛqueezes

Recoil plate pin

Recoil plate

Hammer
This weapon will not fire even if the hammer is struck or dropped while being thumbed back as the hammer nose rests on the frame, not the firing pin.

Firing pin spring

Cylinder release button

Transfer bar
This safety feature means that the weapon can only be fired by pressure on the trigger; the hammer cannot contact the firing pin without the trigger pushing the transfer bar between them. The weapon cannot accidentally fire when dropped on the hammer, as the hammer nose rests on the frame.

Hammer dog pivot pin

Hammer dog spring plunger

Hammer dog

Hammer strut
This connects the hammer to the main spring.

Trigger guard plunger

Grip screw

Trigger guard cross pin

Trigger p
Trigger s
Pawl spri
Pawl plu

Pawl
The pawl engages a ratchet on the ejector and rotates the cylinder, bringing a fresh cartridge into line when the trigger is pulled on double action or when the hammer is pulled back for a single-action shot.

Trigger
There are two different modes of operation with a double-action revolver. When fired single-action, the hammer is cocked back manually with the thumb until it locks. This simultaneously moves the pawl, which rotates the cylinder and moves the trigger back and locks the cylinder latch into the cylinder. Trigger pressure then drops the hammer

and pushes the trans bar into its path to fire weapon. Single-action let-off pressure is considerably less than of double action, and usually used for accu long-range shots. Dou action involves trigge pressure doing all the work, i.e. pulling back hammer, rotating the cylinder and letting th hammer fall etc. This far longer and heavier trigger pull. In training police officers are tau to fire double action a time.

Main spring
The main spring pressure can be adjusted so that it clobbers the percussion cap harder and produces a heavier trigger pull if required. Also, the spring can be adjusted as it wears out.

Grips
Revolvers are improved by the addition of wraparound rubber grips produced by Pachmayr or Hogue. These are designed for combat and greatly improve indexing and control when firing rapid strings of shots.

The golden age of English revolvers

American manufacturers dominate modern revolver production, but this was not always so. During the mid-19th century, several English companies manufactured fine revolvers which gave good service on battlefields from the Crimea to the Indian Mutiny and numerous other engagements. Indeed, the first popular English revolver outshone the famous Colt altogether. The 1851 Adams was a double-action weapon: i.e. pulling the trigger raised the hammer, rotated the cylinder and fired the round all in one movement. On the 1851 Navy Colt, the shooter had to manually cock the hammer first. This made the Adams a better choice for desperate work at close quarters, and British officers testified to its value.

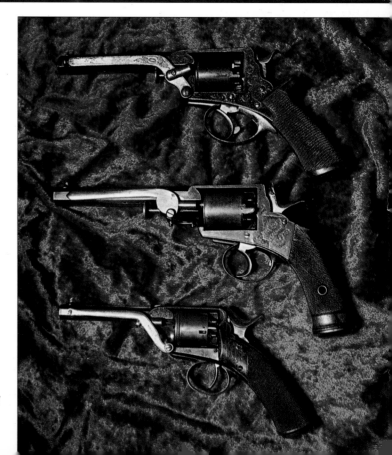

Right, top: The Tranter 54-bore double-action revolver was made under his 1856 patent. The 'L'-shaped lever along the barrel rammed bullets home into the chambers. Middle: The Charles Reeves 54-bore has an inspection plate giving access to the lockwork. Bottom: Henry Ball's 90-bore is one of the rarest 19th century British revolvers, with only a handful of examples known.

Presents from America

During both world wars the British forces' demand for firearms exceeded the manufacturing capacities of both government and private factories. American manufacturers were soon producing weapons under contract. In World War I, Colt supplied large quantities of its .45-calibre New Service model, altered to fire the British .455 round. By 1939 the British Army had

Above: An RAF pilot walks to his aircraft with a Colt .45 revolver tucked into his boot.

The mass of military aid Britain received from the USA under lend-lease included everything from old destroyers to new revolvers like these .38-calibre Smith & Wessons.

Right: American private citizens donated many of their own guns to help Britain at the time when Home Guard units were drilling with broomhandles in 1940.

A rim business

Revolver cartridges have a rim at the base. When the shooter needs to extract the empty cases, he or she pushes the extractor, which acts against the rims, lifting the cases out. But by the time America went to war in 1917, its forces had already abandoned revolvers in favour of the Colt M1911 .45 automatic. Colt could not manufacture enough M1911s to supply the rapidly expanding army and navy, although ammunition was available. Colt and Smith & Wesson

promptly modified their .45-calibre revolvers to shoot the .45 auto cartridge. Because these cartridges have no rim, special fittings were developed to hold them. This meant that they had to be inserted and removed in three-round 'half-moon' clips. These curious hybrid pistols proved very accurate, despite the fiddly loading process. Their popularity is such that Smith & Wesson manufactured a limited run of 5,000 revolvers firing the .45 auto last year. These sought-after guns fetch up to £400 today.

Left: The 1989 limited-edition Smith & Wesson Model 625-2 continues the tradition of firing the .45 ACP cartridge from a revolver. The 625-2 is built from stainless steel with a handsome frosted finish for low reflectivity.

Right: A Ruger Super Redhawk is fired at Bisley, Surrey. The sport of pistol shooting still flourishes in Britain, where the annual pistol event at Bisley is Europe's largest handgun convention. Shooting clubs keep a low profile but can be contacted via newsstand magazines like Target Gun.

Colt .455 New Service

Shown for comparison, the .455 Colt fired a heavy bullet at much lower velocity than modern Magnum ammunition. The vulcanised rubber grips tend to be brittle on a 70-year-old revolver, and they are designed for large hands. Such elderly weapons are still good fun to shoot, but gentle loads must be used. Note that the ejector rod has no protective housing. If it gets bent it is very difficult to unload the weapon.

Ruger Redhawk

The thick topstrap and fat cylinder walls testify to the sturdiness of this .44 Magnum, designed for game-hunting or metallic silhouette shooting. The wooden grips originally supplied have been swapped for rubber ones. Note the coloured foresight: Ruger offers an interchangeable set in yellow, blue, white or red.

Safariland six-round speedloader

Shown filled with .357 Magnum semi-jacketed hollowpoints, this is a typical speedloader, which allows an experienced shooter to reload a revolver in the twinkling of an eye.

S&W 'Horton Special'
This is a customised version of the Model 629: the barrel is cut down to 3 inches and the large butt replaced by the small 'N'-frame type and supplied with wooden grips. The punishing recoil of full power .44 Magnum fired from so short a barrel makes it a good idea to fit rubber grips instead.

Ruger Super Redhawk
The massive frame of the Super Redhawk is designed to take an unvaried diet of full power .44 Magnum ammunition. The 9-in barrel allows it to develop the full potential of the cartridge and a scope mount is provided for long-range shooting.

Ruger GP100
This innovative .357 Magnum is fitted with Ruger's patented cushioned grips that help make firing stiff loads bearable. Integrated sub-assemblies make the GP100 easy to strip down for cleaning. It is very stoutly constructed, both frame sidewalls being solid metal.

standardised on a .38-calibre revolver, but, as the prospect of German invasion increased, public appeals were launched in the USA to provide weapons for Britain. All manner of privately-owned firearms were sent across the Atlantic to help out. Colt and Smith & Wesson shipped generous helpings of their .38-calibre revolvers, which were used by officers, vehicle crew and airmen. Guy Gibson, leader of the famous Dambusters raid, and Stanford Tuck, one of the RAF's best fighter pilots, both carried Smith & Wessons.

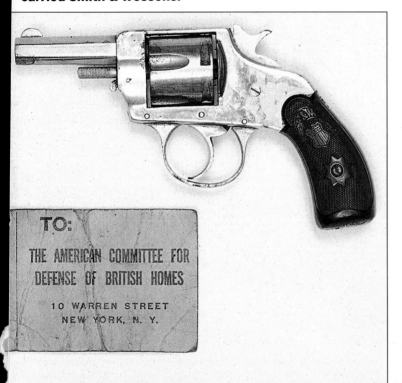

The most powerful handgun in the world

Smith & Wesson's .357 Magnum cartridge sold well enough to sustain commercial interest in even more powerful revolvers. In 1953, the firm introduced the .44 Magnum, which was an instant success with the handgun hunters. It received its greatest commercial boost when Clint Eastwood strode forth with a Model 29 and some great one-liners in the movie *Dirty Harry*. The punk on the sidewalk may not have been feeling lucky, but Smith & Wesson certainly was. The .44 Magnum continues to be popular, and the Smith & Wesson model has now been joined by several Rugers and the new Colt 'Anaconda'. The accolade bestowed by Dirty Harry was lost during the 1970s as a succession of very powerful automatic pistols entered the market. But the world's most awesome handgun remains a revolver: the .454 Casull is a five-shot monster that fires special cartridges more powerful than many intended for hunting rifles.

Above: The 1988 limited-edition Smith & Wesson .44 Magnum 'Classic Hunter' is aimed at the expanding sport of handgun hunting in the USA. The full-length rib beneath the barrel protects the extractor and helps counter the recoil of the powerful cartridge. The hollow lead heads of these semi-jacketed cartridges are clearly visible. This combination allows maximum expansion, while the copper jacket reduces the lead fouling in the barrel.

Above: The five-shot single-action .454 Casull is the most powerful handgun in the world. Fired from a weak grip, it can rebound to strike the shooter on the head!

Right: The awesome muzzle flash of the 3-inch barrel .44 Magnum Horton Special.

Designer guns

The sport of pistol shooting became popular during the 19th century, and several manufacturers introduced specialist revolvers intended to win competitions rather than battles. As revolvers have ceased to be used as military weapons, police-style shooting competitions have developed. Emphasising speed as well as accuracy, they are a far cry from traditional precision shooting. The Davis series of custom-built revolvers is one of several weapons designed for these new shooting disciplines. Heavyweight barrels keep the centre of gravity towards the muzzle, which prevents the gun straying too far off target after the first round. The action is exceptional, making standard commercial revolvers seem stiff and clumsy. Prices start at around £600 and spiral upwards to five or six times the cost of a typical large-frame .38.

Correct trigger-finger position for double-action shooting, as demonstrated on a Davis custom .38 revolver.

Above: Throwing money at your shooting does not guarantee victory in competitions, but weapons like this Davis can give competitors a dramatic edge. The 'aristocratic rib' adjustable sights and a double action smoother than silk underwear make it the most accurate revolver available.

THE GUNS OF AUGUST

British soldiers of 1914 carried the most powerful handgun of its day. From the trenches of Flanders to the African bush and Arabian desert, the .455-calibre Webley served them well.

Left: Wearing respirators to protect themselves against poison gas, British soldiers scramble out of a shell hole. The officer carries a Webley Mk V revolver.

The column of troops halted again as a group of officers hastily conferred on the roadside. The brief summer night was nearly over and the battalion was still far behind the enemy lines. Their route to safety ran through the small village of Clary, but the Germans had got there first. The Gordon Highlanders had been cut off during the battle of Le Cateau on 26 August 1914.

Finally withdrawing near dusk, they had precious little time to slip away to rejoin the retreating British Army.

A succession of brief shoot-outs with German detachments had resulted in several casualties, and it was clear that unless an escape route could be discovered, the battalion would have to surrender. The stand at Le Cateau had held off the vastly superior German

forces for a day, but now the rest of British II Corps was hurrying westwards to escape encirclement. What German forces were in Clary? A group of officers slipped ahead to see.

They soon discovered that an inn had been taken over by a group of German officers. Relaxing in the belief that the British were in headlong retreat, the Germans had paid little

attention to their own security. The British officers drew their revolvers and gathered at the door. In an instant they were inside and the small bar amplified the deafening blast of their .455-calibre pistols. It was all over in a moment. Taken completely by surprise, the Germans died with wine glasses in their hands.

With the opposition speedily overcome, the Gordons hurried through, but elements of the German 66th Infantry Regiment were already ahead of them. They ran into the enemy on the other side of the village, and after an hour-long exchange of gunfire, dawn was breaking and the British were surrounded. Running out of ammunition and with no hope of escape, the column was forced to surrender. The scene of the Gordons' last stand changed little during the war, since it was behind the German lines. When British official historians compiled a guide to the battlefield during the 1930s, the walls of the inn at Clary still showed the bullet marks left by the officers' revolvers.

British officers were issued with the Webley .455 service revolver. A robust handgun produced with either a 4- or 6-inch barrel, it fired a much more

Above left: An officer leads a party of troops forward through the remains of a wood. This desolation, caused by artillery bombardment, puts the military value of the revolver into perspective.

Above: A British officer holds his Webley at the ready near the river Aisne on 27 May 1918, the day the German army smashed another hole in the Allied lines.

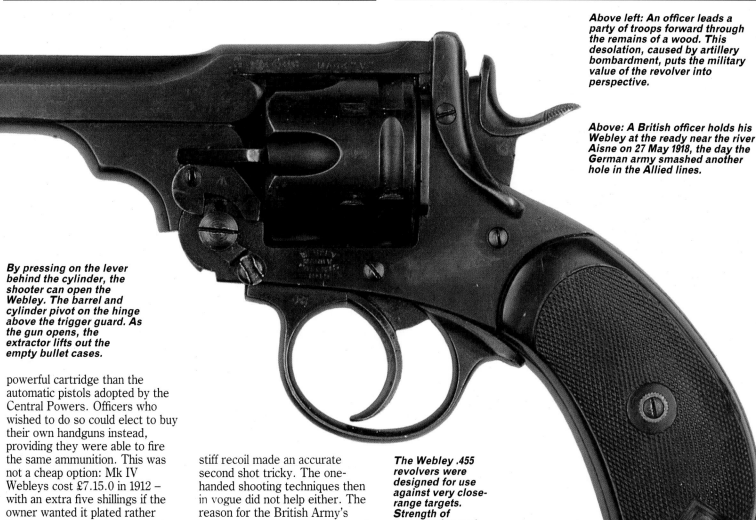

By pressing on the lever behind the cylinder, the shooter can open the Webley. The barrel and cylinder pivot on the hinge above the trigger guard. As the gun opens, the extractor lifts out the empty bullet cases.

The Webley .455 revolvers were designed for use against very close-range targets. Strength of construction and reliability were more important than target accuracy. Even the target model, the WG, proved a successful combat weapon.

powerful cartridge than the automatic pistols adopted by the Central Powers. Officers who wished to do so could elect to buy their own handguns instead, providing they were able to fire the same ammunition. This was not a cheap option: Mk IV Webleys cost £7.15.0 in 1912 – with an extra five shillings if the owner wanted it plated rather than in service blued finish. But the Webley WG target revolver with its 7½-inch barrel and adjustable sights cost £12, and eccentric weapons like the Webley-Fosbery even more. The WG was a fine combat revolver, accurate and reliable yet not too cumbersome for desperate close-quarter battle. The price hardly troubled an officer corps which was, after all, London Society in khaki.

The .455 cartridge was difficult for a beginner to master. Its fairly stiff recoil made an accurate second shot tricky. The one-handed shooting techniques then in vogue did not help either. The reason for the British Army's insistence on this powerful round was the importance of 'stopping power': in colonial conflicts against fanatical opponents like the Zulu or Sudanese tribesmen it was vital to stop the enemy with a single round. Experience showed that the bigger bounding savage was unimpressed with a small pistol round. The US Army encountered the same problem in the Philippines and reached the same conclusion; the Americans adopted the famous .45 Automatic Colt Pistol cartridge.

Above: Troops light up while the officer studies his orders. He seems to have removed the top flap of his holster for speedier access to his revolver.

Below: Going 'over the top', the officer grips his revolver, finger on the trigger: a good reason for having a stiff trigger pull. With a light trigger, he is likely to shoot the man to his right by accident!

The British Army managed to elude the Germans in several weeks of hard marching after Le Cateau. A series of fierce battles in October and November left the Allied and German armies facing each other in positions that would hardly change in the next four years. In the trench warfare that followed, short-range weapons like grenades and pistols became more important. On battlefields dominated by artillery and machine-guns, infantrymen usually found themselves fighting at close quarters: slugging it out to win control of a section of trench or a well-placed shellhole.

Revolvers also took to the air. The aircraft flown during 1914-15 were mostly unarmed, but the more sporting aircrew flew with handguns or hunting rifles with which to engage their opposite numbers if they encountered them. But the war became a nastier business in the air as well as on the ground. Sitting next to an unsealed tank of petrol in a canvas and wood aircraft, pilots were soon fighting it out with machine-guns. Awaiting them all was an horrific death in a burning machine fluttering to earth from 10,000 feet. Most of Manfred von Richthofen's 80 'kills' went down in flames. Some pilots openly carried revolvers with them, to go out less painfully.

The battle of the Somme began on 1 July 1916. The most carefully prepared British attempt to break through the German lines, it produced the longest casualty list in British military history up till then. But although thousands of troops were killed before they even reached the German lines, some units did penetrate the German defences. A soldier of the Ulster Division describes their battle inside the enemy lines. It was a brutal struggle at close quarters, where rifles were replaced by pistols, home-made clubs and hand grenades.

Revolvers and bayonets

"We had a man from Roslea with us and he did a bit of poaching and he could move without making a sound, so he and the sergeant set off first. The sergeant could clout a bomb further than any other man I knew. We were to leave in pairs counting 20 between each pair and the next . . . I had a bayonet in one hand and a revolver in the other. You see, I used to shoe horses before I joined up and had powerful strong wrists, and it was not a great hardship for me to fire one of those big heavy revolvers. They had a kick like a horse but if you hit a man with a bullet from one of them he gave no more trouble . . . we all made our way down to the third line . . . here there was one young officer . . . and he set about getting us set for a bayonet charge against the trenches in front of us – the Crucifix . . . we fixed bayonets and charged. There were not many Germans left alive. Few of us got hit on the dash across; maybe we caught the Germans off guard . . . we cleared the trenches right down to the Mouquet Switch – we settled down to the bit we captured. We took no prisoners and did not have to detail any men to guard duty."

In the narrow confines of a trench system, a revolver made better sense than a rifle. The enemy were liable to appear from unexpected angles, emerging from dug-outs or counter-attacking from a nearby shell crater. They were also likely to

Left and above: The Colt New Service was supplied to the British Army from 1915 to 1918. Originally chambered for the .45 Colt, it needed only minor modifications to take the standard British service cartridge. Introduced in 1898, the New Service was ultimately manufactured in 18 different calibres! This is an early-model .455 example, recognisable by its fine charcoal blue finish.

Below: In the harsh conditions of the Western Front, only the most robust weapons and equipment could be relied upon. Revolvers were preferable to many early 20th century automatic pistols, which proved too fragile in action.

be very close, and bayonet fighting occurred with terrifying frequency. Robert Graves discovered a British and a German soldier who had simultaneously bayoneted each other to death.

Pistols did have their obvious limitations: they were still inaccurate unless the shooter was particularly well-practised, and the six-shot capacity of a revolver's cylinder could not sustain a gunfight for very long. When American troops went into action in 1918, they experimented with pump-action shotguns. Better suited to instinctive close-range shooting, their Winchester Model 1897 shotguns proved highly effective. Some were fitted with a bayonet attachment in case soldiers encountered a similarly armed opponent at the wrong moment.

SMG answer

The Germans relied on Mauser pistols with shoulder-stocks that converted them into carbines for engaging more distant targets. But the real answer, of course, was the sub-machine gun, and several countries were developing them as the war ended. The renowned Thompson .45 SMG was designed expressly for trench fighting, but was not completed in time to use in the war. By World War II, SMGs were in service with all major armies and the pistol's military role was as a personal defence weapon for officers and vehicle crew.

Miami policemen in uniform and in plain clothes cover a suspect with their revolvers during a drugs raid in which eight people were arrested. The real world of drug enforcement is very different from its popular image – one episode of Miami Vice cost more than the real vice department's annual budget.

WATCH AND SHOOT

Statistics from the USA show that when law enforcement officers have to use their guns the average range is only two or three metres. Not surprisingly, the average number of rounds fired is low, with fewer than three shots normally required to resolve the situation. But officers must train for the exceptional cases, mastering longer ranges and difficult firing positions, if they are to be fully prepared.

Revolvers are very straightforward weapons, which makes them ideal for police use. Contrary to TV cop-shows, police officers in the USA and Europe spend very little of their time shooting unless they belong to a specialist unit: for most of the time, the revolver is simply another piece of kit to be carried around. But although simple to operate, a revolver does demand regular training if it is to be effective. Issuing revolvers to officers who then hardly fire a shot in practice has led to serious problems in several countries. The difficulty faced by many departments is – as always – money. Maintaining an officer's revolver shooting at a high standard requires several hours' practice and 100-150 rounds of ammunition every week. In reality, this is only possible for special formations which anticipate using their weapons in anger on a regular basis.

1 Drawing from the holster

Holster design is a necessary compromise between speedy access to the gun and security when it is not in use. Many law enforcement personnel have to battle their way past security straps or top flaps to get at their revolvers. They are trained never to insert their finger through the trigger guard while drawing the weapon. Yanking a loaded revolver out of a holster with a finger on the trigger is a good way to shoot yourself in the foot.

2 Sight picture

Unless the felon is close enough to blow his last breath in the officer's face, proper use of sights is important. Unless in a particularly unusual situation, the objective is to end the action with a few well-aimed shots. It is particularly important to practise drawing the gun and acquiring a clear sight picture as rapidly as possible.

3 Trigger control

For the best controlled double-action shooting, the forefinger is positioned so the first joint pivots over the trigger. The revolver is fired two-handed, the supporting hand gripping around the one holding the gun. The key to success is a swift but smooth trigger pull. Panicky snatching at the trigger can produce a miss even at incredibly short ranges.

4 Weaver stance

Los Angeles County Deputy Sheriff Jack Weaver developed this shooting stance, which has now become very popular. If shooting right-handed, the left shoulder faces the target, with the left arm bent and the left hand applying isometric pressure against the right hand. The right arm is either locked straight or slightly bent, depending on the shooter's preference. This stance suits the carefully aimed shot or rapid snap-shot equally well.

5 Isosceles stance

This is the classic 'square-on' position in which the officer faces the target, arms extended. For some reason, TV cop-shows keep showing their stars running about with their guns pointed at the sky. They aim their handguns at a steep angle as if engaging hostile aircraft, then bring the weapon horizontal to shoot. This is a great way to put a round into orbit, but wastes vital time getting the gun on target.

Above and right: Old military-style holsters are unsuited for a quick draw, since the shooter must get the top flap out of the way before reaching for his weapon. Here US Marines draw their 4-inch barrel Ruger .357 Security Six revolvers, which are issued to the security detachments posted at US embassies.

Left: Cartridge belt loops were the standard method of carrying ammunition until the 1970s, when speed-loading devices were introduced by several police departments.

Below: This commercially-produced police belt rig in black Cordura nylon comes from 'Uncle Mike's', the US gun accessory manufacturer.

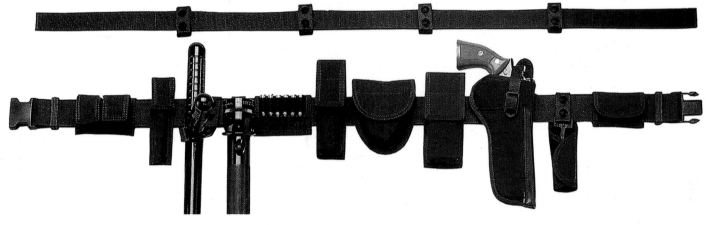

Above: The increasing popular sport of 'practical pistol' emphasises the speedy but safe use of handguns. Here the shooter must open the door and engage several targets in rapid succession.

6 Shooting kneeling

When shooting from behind low obstacles, a stable kneeling position is a great aid to accuracy. The shooter rests the elbow of his supporting arm on his knee and leans slightly towards the target. The alternative kneeling posture – with both knees on the ground – is fine for target shooting but limits a shooter's options in a gunfight.

7 Sitting position

The sitting position is used in several target shooting competitions but is not appropriate for combat shooting. The only situation where it might perhaps be relevant would be in an ambush. It is essentially a long-range shooting position, but if officers find themselves shooting it out at 50-100 metres with handguns, something has gone seriously wrong.

8 Barricade shooting

If shooting around a wall or similar obstacle, it is important to use the cover available. US Customs and Secret Service shooting teams can achieve 5-inch groups at 50 yards using the correct barricade technique. Positioning themselves a pace behind the barricade, they lean forward with their left hand resting against it. Left-handed shooting is essential, since targets do not always oblige by appearing around the right-hand side of cover.

9 Speed-reloading

For many years, police officers in the USA carried extra rounds in cartridge loops on their belts. After some reluctance, most police departments now accept the use of speed-loading devices. These hold six rounds ready to insert in the cylinder, so all the shooter needs to do is eject his spent cartridge cases and slip in a fresh load. Partial reloading – replacing the odd one or two rounds fired – is fine as long as the shooter is certain he cannot be surprised in the act.

Above: The PAA (Police Athletic Association) target used in the sport of 'Police Pistol' faces the shooter for only a few seconds. Maximum points are scored by hitting the centre ring around the paper villain's gun.

Speed-loaders allow the shooter to reload his or her revolver in one swift movement, rather than having to fiddle with individual bullets.

10 Identify the threat

The use of firearms for law enforcement places a heavy burden on the police, who cannot simply open fire the moment a target presents itself: there is always the chance of encountering innocent civilians. The felon may have no hesitation in shooting anyone he runs into during a shoot-out, but law enforcement officers have to be more circumspect. The best answer is to move about in the Weaver 'ready' position. If a potential target appears, officers must identify it within the time it takes to move the revolver from the 'ready' position into the 'aim'.